WORD WIZARD

Literacy Skills and Activities

Jane O'Loughlin

GILL EDUCATION

Contents

			Page
How to Use this Book			iv–v
Instructions for Phonics Games			vi

Unit / Genre	Skill	Topic	Page
UNIT 1: Artwork	Phonics Game	ch, sh, th and wh; ll, ff, ss and zz; ck, ng and nk; Magic e	1
	Reading, Comprehension, Oral Language	'Girl with a Boat' by Pablo Picasso	2–3
	Phonics	ch, sh, th and wh; ll, ff, ss and zz; ck, ng and nk; Magic e	4
	Grammar	Capital Letters 1	5
	Writing Genre	Fact File (My Passport)	6
UNIT 2: Explanatory Text 1	Phonics Game	/ee/ sound family – ee, y, ea; /ai/ sound family – ai, a_e, ay	7
	Reading, Comprehension, Oral Language	Why Do Animals Hibernate?	8–9
	Phonics	/ee/ sound family – ee, y, ea; /ai/ sound family – ai, a_e, ay	10
	Grammar	Capital Letters 2	11
	Writing Genre	Parts of an Explanatory Text (Why Do Animals Hibernate?)	12
UNIT 3: Explanatory Text 2	Phonics Game	/oa/ sound family – oa, o_e, ow; /ie/ sound family – ie, i_e, y, igh	13
	Reading, Comprehension, Oral Language	Why Do Some Trees Drop Their Leaves?	14–15
	Phonics	/oa/ sound family – oa, o_e, ow; /ie/ sound family – ie, i_e, y, igh	16
	Grammar	Verbs	17
	Writing Genre	Modelled and Shared Writing (The Life-cycle of an Oak Tree)	18
UNIT 4: Explanatory Text 3	Phonics Game	/ue/ sound family – ue, u_e, ew; /ou/ sound family – ou, ow	19
	Reading, Comprehension, Oral Language	Was Count Dracula Real?	20–21
	Phonics	/ue/ sound family – ue, u_e, ew; /ou/ sound family – ou, ow	22
	Grammar	Alphabetical Order	23
	Writing Genre	Independent Writing (Why We Brush our Teeth)	24
UNIT 5: Recount 1	Phonics Game	/ool/ sound family – le; /u/ sound family – ou	25
	Reading, Comprehension, Oral Language	Minding Baby Elle	26–27
	Phonics	/ool/ sound family – le; /u/ sound family – ou	28
	Grammar	Past Tense Verbs – 'ed', Doubling / 1:1:1 Rule	29
	Writing Genre	Parts of a Recount (Minding Baby Elle)	30
UNIT 6: Recount 2	Phonics Game	/sh/ sound family – sion, tion	31
	Reading, Comprehension, Oral Language	TVFlicks.com	32–33
	Phonics	/sh/ sound family – sion, tion	34
	Grammar	Past Tense Irregular Verbs	35
	Writing Genre	Modelled and Shared Writing (School Event)	36
UNIT 7: Recount 3	Phonics Game	/ai/ sound family – ei, eigh; /f/ sound family – ph	37
	Reading, Comprehension, Oral Language	Rudolph's Diary	38–39
	Phonics	/ai/ sound family – ei, eigh; /f/ sound family – ph	40
	Grammar	Nouns	41
	Writing Genre	Independent Writing (Christmas)	42
UNIT 8: Revision and Assessment	Revision	Grammar and Phonics	43–44
	Assessment	Phonics	45
	Reading	Rover Saves Christmas	46
	Assessment	Comprehension and Vocabulary	47
	Assessment	Grammar	48
UNIT 9: Report 1	Phonics Game	Soft c; /au/ sound family – au, al, aw	49
	Reading, Comprehension, Oral Language	The Polar Bear	50–51
	Phonics	Soft c; /au/ sound family – au, al, aw	52
	Grammar	Adjectives 1	53
	Writing Genre	Parts of a Report and Modelled and Shared Writing (The Seal)	54

Unit / Genre	Skill	Topic	Page
UNIT 10: Report 2	Phonics Game	/ee/ sound family – ey, ie; Silent w	55
	Reading, Comprehension, Oral Language	Celebrating Chinese New Year	56–57
	Phonics	/ee/ sound family – ey, ie; Silent w	58
	Grammar	Adjectives 2	59
	Writing Genre	Independent Writing (The Walrus)	60
UNIT 11: Poetry	Phonics Game	ture; /ur/ sound family – er, ir, ur	61
	Reading, Comprehension, Oral Language	'On the Ning Nang Nong' by Spike Milligan	62–63
	Phonics	ture; /ur/ sound family – er, ir, ur	64
	Grammar	Capital Letters 3	65
	Writing Genre	Independent Writing (Nonsense Poem)	66
UNIT 12: Procedure 1	Phonics Game	Silent k; Silent h	67
	Reading, Comprehension, Oral Language	How to Make Pancakes	68–69
	Phonics	Silent k; Silent h	70
	Grammar	'Bossy' (Command) Verbs	71
	Writing Genre	Parts of a Procedure (How to Make Pancakes)	72
UNIT 13: Procedure 2	Phonics Game	Silent b; Silent c	73
	Reading, Comprehension, Oral Language	How to Make a Bubble Bomb	74–75
	Phonics	Silent b; Silent c	76
	Grammar	Plural – 'es'	77
	Writing Genre	Modelled and Shared Writing (Apple Pop Snacks)	78
UNIT 14: Procedure 3	Phonics Game	/oi/ sound family – oi, oy; Soft g	79
	Reading, Comprehension, Oral Language	Game: Cowboys and Robbers	80–81
	Phonics	/oi/ sound family – oi, oy; Soft g	82
	Grammar	Plural – 'ies'	83
	Writing Genre	Independent Writing (Banana Blast Smoothie)	84
UNIT 15: Narrative 1	Phonics Game	/e/ sound family – ea	85
	Reading, Comprehension, Oral Language	The Gingerbread Man	86–87
	Phonics	/e/ sound family – ea	88
	Grammar	Connecting Words	89
	Writing Genre	Parts of a Narrative (The Gingerbread Man)	90
UNIT 16: Narrative 2	Phonics Game	/or/ sound family – or, ore; /air/ sound family – air	91
	Reading, Comprehension, Oral Language	Horrid Henry's Holiday	92–93
	Phonics	/or/ sound family – or, ore; /air/ sound family – air	94
	Grammar	Speech Marks	95
	Writing	Modelled and Shared Writing (Imaginative Story)	96
UNIT 17: Narrative 3	Vocabulary	Revision of Homophones	97
	Reading, Comprehension, Oral Language	'The Dinosaur's Dinner' by June Crebbin	98–99
	Phonics	/k/ sound family – ch	100
	Grammar	Tired Words – 'said'	101
	Writing	Independent Writing (Imaginative Story)	102
UNIT 18: Revision and Assessment	Revision	Grammar and Phonics	103–104
	Assessment	Phonics	105
	Reading	Grandad's Mad Garden	106
	Assessment	Comprehension and Vocabulary	107
	Assessment	Grammar	108
Dictation			109–110

How to Use this Book

Phonics games

This book contains four different kinds of phonics game, one of which is used on the first page of every unit to introduce the sounds being taught. Nonsense words have been included in the games to encourage pupils to practise their decoding skills and to challenge those who have a tendency to learn words by sight.

A monkey or a raccoon character appears at the bottom of the page, offering tips on how to replay the game at home to further consolidate learning.

Detailed instructions for playing the phonics games can be found on page vi.

Phonics linked with comprehension

Vocabulary containing the sounds taught within the unit has been incorporated into the comprehension reading passages wherever possible. This helps to bridge the gap between phonics and real reading practice, rather than teaching both in isolation. An owl character appears before each reading passage, asking pupils to look out for certain sounds in the text.

Vocabulary development

A meerkat character appears before each reading passage, asking pupils to explain the bold words in the text to their partner or to look them up in a dictionary (from Unit 9 onwards) before reading. This is designed to facilitate the teaching of tricky vocabulary prior to reading the text.

Higher order comprehension questions

At this level, pupils are introduced to answering written, higher order thinking questions.

Genre writing

This book takes a unique approach to genre writing. The reading passage serves as a template for the genre. The teacher can refer to this while outlining the parts (structure) of the genre, by asking pupils to highlight or use yellow stickies to identify various elements. Discrete oral language activities act as building blocks for genre writing, and grammar activities are linked to the genre wherever appropriate.

At this level, genre writing usually follows a six-week approach, with a fortnight spent on each unit. Generally, three units are dedicated to each genre as follows: the first explores the parts of the genre, the second presents both modelled and shared writing experiences and the third gives pupils an opportunity to write independently. (Please note that report writing differs in that it is covered over four weeks.)

Detailed teaching notes are available online, outlining the steps for progressing through each of the stages. YouTube links have been included to act as a stimulus for writing wherever appropriate.

Dictation

Two dictation sentences are provided for each unit, incorporating the phonics and grammar taught. Suggestions are provided for extension activities or further revision of grammar. Differentiation is also catered for.

Assessment

A self-assessment feature appears below each dictation activity.

Two units dedicated to revision and assessment are provided at the end of the second and third terms. Each includes a special four-day section designed to prompt meaningful revision of phonics and grammar before assessment begins.

Editable writing frames and self-assessment checklists

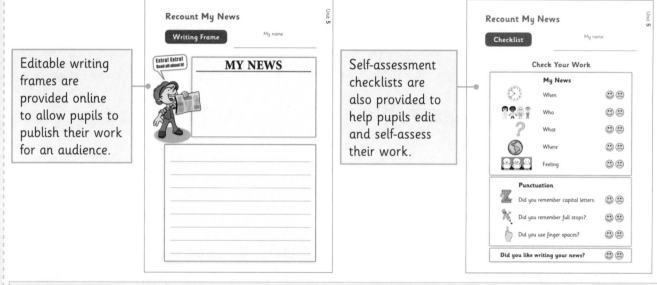

Editable writing frames are provided online to allow pupils to publish their work for an audience.

Self-assessment checklists are also provided to help pupils edit and self-assess their work.

Key to online resource symbols

Oral language
Indicates that a detailed oral language activity is available online.

Discussion genre text
Indicates that an excerpt from another text, highlighting features of a particular genre, and accompanying teacher's notes are available online.

Modelled or shared writing experience
Indicates that a modelled writing activity with accompanying teacher's notes is available online or that the activity book itself presents an opportunity for a shared writing activity. (Please note that most shared writing activities do not come with teacher's notes. These follow on from modelled writing activities, in which the teacher acts as scribe while the class contributes ideas.)

Printable
Both a writing template and a self-assessment checklist for each genre are available online.

Instructions for Phonics Games

A spin and a roll

What you will need:

- two players ▪ a die ▪ two pencils

How to play

1. Practise reading all of the words before you begin.
2. Roll the die. The player with the highest number goes first.
3. They must read any word from the column that corresponds to the number on the die. If they read it correctly, they can ring the word.
4. The second player takes their turn.
5. The winner is the first player to ring all of the words in a column.

Four in a row

What you will need:

- two players ▪ a die ▪ two counters

How to play

1. Practise reading all of the words before you begin.
2. Roll the die. The player with the highest number goes first.
3. They must read a word from any box that corresponds to the number on the die. If they read it correctly, they can place a counter on the word.
4. The winner is the first player to get four in a row vertically, horizontally or diagonally.

Snakes and Ladders

What you will need:

- two players ▪ a die ▪ two counters

How to play

1. Practise reading all of the words before you begin.
2. Place your counters on **start**.
3. Roll the die. The player with the highest number goes first.
4. Take turns rolling the die and moving the correct number of places.
5. Sound out each word that you land on.
6. If you land on a ladder, move up.
7. If you land on a snake, move down.
8. The winner is the first player to reach the **finish** line.

Roll and read

What you will need:

- two players ▪ a die ▪ two counters

How to play

1. Practise reading all of the words before you begin.
2. Place your counters on **start**.
3. Roll the die. The player with the highest number goes first.
4. Take turns rolling the die and moving the correct number of places.
5. Sound out each word that you land on.
6. If you read it correctly, you may stay there. If you read it incorrectly, you must go back to where you were.
7. The winner is the first player to reach the **finish** line.

Teacher's Notes

Section A introduces sounds taught in the unit and recaps on sounds from earlier units. Please note that not all of these sounds are incorporated into the game.

The following suggestions can help to ensure that the words in the game are read correctly:

- Read all of the words as a whole-class activity before playing the game.
- Model playing the game in pairs, demonstrating how pupils should read the word that their partner has landed on in order to check that their partner has read it correctly.
- Divide pupils into reading groups. Sit with the weakest group most of the time, but visit another group. The game could be played for a short period on three consecutive days.
- The game could be assigned for homework.

'Girl with a Boat'

Phonics Game

| ch, sh, th and wh | ck, ng, and nk |
| ll, ff, ss and zz | Magic e |

A Before you begin the game, tick (✓) the sounds that you are able to read. 🖉

| ck | | ch | | ff | | ss | | ng | | i_e | | sh | |
| th | | wh | | o_e | | zz | | sw | | a_e | | u_e | |

B A spin and a roll

We all say nonsense words!

•	••	•••	••••	•••••	••••••
wheelchair	whicken	brupe	blick	different	trize
brilliant	frilliant	ratch	possop	blust	snule
frunk	stomping	muffin	tuffin	fromp	sunglasses
shunder	crisps	rubbish	difficult	second	whale
frope	skunk	stripe	popbleeper	broke	glisp
matchstick	shopkeeper	thrillent	swave	flute	mecond
spade	glizz	lollipop	frozen	include	gifferent
spode	dubbish	sticker	inside	smifficult	whisker

Try playing this with two players at home. Simply rub out the words you have ringed in class. This time, Player One can underline words and Player Two can ring them. Whoever fills a column first wins!

Comprehension

Looking at Art – 'Girl With a Boat'

'Girl With a Boat' was painted by Pablo Picasso. His father was an art teacher and an artist. He started teaching his son art when he was seven years old. Picasso finished his first painting when he was just nine years old.

Picasso was a great artist, but he didn't want to paint like everyone else. He really liked children's art. He loved how children use lots of colours and shapes in their pictures. He also liked the way children's pictures do not look real. He started to paint like this and other artists did too. This type of art is called Cubism, because the pictures have lots of cubes and other shapes.

Picasso liked to paint pictures of his own children. The girl in this picture is his daughter. Her name was Maya. He painted lots of pictures of her.

A In your copy, go investigate.

1. Who painted this picture?

2. How old was he when he finished his first painting? *9yrs*

3. What do you see in the picture?

4. Does the girl look real?

5. What is the girl holding?

6. What colours do you see?

7. The picture has lots of shapes. Can you name them?

B In your copy, give your opinion.

1. Why do you think the girl is clutching her boat?

2. Where do you think she is? Is she indoors or outdoors?

3. How do you think she feels?

4. What colours would you use to paint a happy picture of yourself?

5. What item would you hold in your picture? Why?

C Vocabulary: Match each word to its opposite.

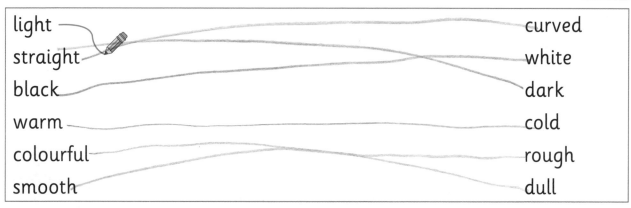

light   curved
straight   white
black   dark
warm   cold
colourful   rough
smooth   dull

Phonics

ch, sh, th and wh	ck, ng, and nk
ll, ff, ss and zz	Magic e

A Look at each picture. Tick (✓) the correct word.

kitchen		selfish		whisper	✓
ketchup	✓	shelter		whisker	
kangaroo		shellfish	✓	whimper	
trumpet		unless		beehive	✓
ticket		unpack		bedtime	
toothbrush	✓	umbrella	✓	bullring	
bucket		perfume		smelled	✓
buzzer	✓	packet		smack	
blanket		pancake	✓	smash	
stone		husband		chitchat	
stove		hairdresser		chopsticks	✓
stamp	✓	hatstand	✓	cheese	

B Write the correct word.

1. I got a *packet* of crisps in the shop. **pocket / packet**

2. Dave asked the waitress for a muffin and a *scone* .
   scone / scales

3. Danaka spilled the paint on the *ground* .
   grape / ground

4. I got a sticker when I finished the *difficult* worksheet.
   difficult / different

5. My dad *snores* when he falls asleep. **snores / smells**

6. My gran lost her glasses and I *found* them on a shelf.
   frozen / found / frame

Strand: Reading Element: Understanding LO 4, 5

Grammar – Capital Letters 1

A Write the correct word.

We use a capital letter…

1. At the start of a *sentence*   **sentence / book / newspaper**

2. For a person's *name* .   **age / name**

3. For the name of a *animal* .   **place / animal / food**

4. For a *day* of the week.   **month / time / day**

5. For a *month* of the year.   **day / month / name**

6. For the word '*me* '.   **me / am / I**

B Ring the word that does not need a capital letter.

1. (Raincoat)	Saturday	Billy	Thomas
2. Zara	September	(Cheese)	Rebecca
3. Sandra	(Sunny)	Patrick	Ireland
4. Film	Longford	Limerick	Scotland
5. Week	Monday	Tuesday	Wednesday
6. January	Saturday	Year	(March)

C Ring the words that need a capital letter.

(my) name is (freddy. (i) am seven years old. (i) live in (greenwoods) in (dublin. (my) mum is called (tessa) and my dad is called (jack. (on) sundays we like to go to the park on our bikes. sometimes we play football. the park is called (greenhills) park. (we) often bring our dog, spike, along, but we must bring a plastic bag to clean up his poop!

D Dictation: Listen to your teacher and write the sentences.

1. _____

2. _____

How did you do? 🙂 ⚪ 😐 ⚪ 🙁 ⚪

Writing Genre – Fact File

A Fill in your profile below.

My Passport

Draw a selfie.

All about me

Name: Seán cannon

Age: 7 years old

Hair colour: brown

Eye colour: eye

Class: 2 ed

My favourite things

Food: chips gousham

Colour: blue

TV programme: Thomas and friends

Toy: Trasi

Book:

Music:

Subject:

My family

Draw and label your family members.

Why Animals Hibernate 2

Phonics Game | /ee/ sound family – ee, y, ea | /ai/ sound family – ai, a_e, ay

A Before you begin the game, tick (✓) the sounds that you are able to read. ✏️

ll		ai		ee		wh		ch		y		a_e	
ay		ea		ck		y		nk		a_e		lt	

B Four in a row

1 cheeky	2 plane	3 drave	4 rainy	5 tainy	6 crayon
1 paintbrush	2 blay	3 stray	4 sneaky	5 raindrop	6 bleaty
1 gleeze	2 greedy	3 dreaky	4 smay	5 maintshush	6 squeaky
1 crane	2 thumb	3 sticky	4 drumpy	5 freaky	6 chase
1 crusty	2 daisy	3 dreech	4 creepy	5 shave	6 snayon
1 spray	2 brusty	3 creaky	4 frane	5 twenty	6 playroom

Try playing this at home again. All you need is a die and a set of counters.

Strand: Reading Element: Understanding LO 4, 5

Comprehension

Do you know what the **bold** words below mean? Can you explain them to your partner?

Look out for words from the /ai/ and /ee/ sound families in the explanation below.

Why Do Animals Hibernate?

Hibernation is when animals go into a deep sleep during the winter months and do not wake up until springtime. There are lots of animals that hibernate, including hedgehogs, bats, frogs, squirrels and insects.

In winter, it gets very cold and it is **difficult** for animals to find food. We all need food to live. It gives us the **energy** we use to breathe, eat, drink and even to think. It is easy for humans to find food in winter. All we need to do is go shopping. Animals must go into a deep sleep instead.

A hedgehog making a nest

To **prepare** for the deep sleep, they build up **layers** of fat under their skin. They do this by eating large amounts of food in autumn. Then, they find somewhere **suitable** to sleep. This might be in a ditch, beneath a pile of branches or even inside a cave. When they go to sleep, their body **temperature** drops, their heartbeat slows down and it is very hard to wake them. They save their energy by not running around, and **survive** on the fat stored under their skin instead of eating food. They sleep like this throughout the winter. Some animals wake up for a short time on

warmer days and look for a snack that they may have hidden nearby.

Finally, the animals wake up in springtime when food becomes easier to find once again.

Did you know that some animals go into such a deep sleep that they may appear to be dead?

A squirrel eating lots of nuts

A In your copy, go investigate. 🔍

1. Name four animals that hibernate.

2. What do animals do when they hibernate?

3. How is food useful to us?

4. How do some animals build up layers of fat for winter?

5. What happens to animals when they fall into a deep sleep?

6. Why do animals wake up again in springtime?

B In your copy, give your opinion. 💭

1. Do you think animals are clever for hibernating in winter? Why?

2. How do you think the animals feel when they wake up in spring?

3. What food might not be available to insects in winter?

4. Otters are fish-eating animals. Do you think they hibernate? Why?

C Vocabulary: Write the correct word. ✏️

to	**too**	**see**	**sea**

1. I will give a present _____ Emily.

2. I went _____ the park yesterday.

3. Can I go to the shops _____ ?

4. We have _____ do our homework every night.

5. Did you know that Harry has a dog _____ ?

6. Last summer we swam in the _____ .

7. Will I _____ you tomorrow at football practice?

8. I cannot _____ the board from here.

9. My friend Ella lives near the _____ .

Phonics /ee/ sound family – ee, y, ea | /ai/ sound family – ai, a_e, ay

You can spell the /ee/ sound using the following letters:

sheep	happy	leaf

You can spell the /ai/ sound using the following letters:

nail	game	crayon

A Fill in the correct word/s from the word box.

buggy   play   muddy   coffee   sleep   carry   rained   made

1. Kate woke up late after a very long _____.

2. I _____ a yummy chocolate cake for Lee.

3. Granny drinks a cup of _____ every morning.

4. Will you _____ the tray into the playroom?

5. It _____ all day and the garden
   was very _____.

6. My little sister likes to _____
   with her dolly in her _____.

B Read each sentence and cross out the incorrect word.

1. Dave put c̶a̶m̶e̶ the train set and games in the playroom.

2. My puppy was greedy filthy when he jumped in the mud.

3. Dee put made the teapot, the milk and the teacup on a tray.

4. Our teacher mum played a funny spelling game with us in class.

5. The captain of our play football team always gives a big scream when we win.

6. Mum said, "I will teach you to clean up that messy cake bedroom."

Strand: Reading Element: Understanding LO 4, 5, 6

Grammar – Capital Letters 2

A Ring the word that does not need a capital letter.

1. August   October   Jill   (Doll)
2. Carl   Flour   July   James
3. Scarf   Wexford   Jim   Dublin
4. Saturday   September   Jolly   Monday
5. Kerry   Japan   Fling   Russia
6. Grandad   Clown   March   Mrs Jake

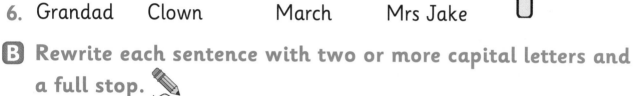

Dublin   50 km

B Rewrite each sentence with two or more capital letters and a full stop.

1. my birthday is in october

_____

2. gran is planning a trip to dublin to visit her friend

_____

3. kevin and yara go to basketball training on wednesday

_____

4. every friday, we do our shopping in supervalu

_____

5. my dog is named spot and my cat is named whiskers

_____

6. the months of autumn are august, september and october

_____

C Dictation: Listen to your teacher and write the sentences.

1. _____

2. _____

How did you do?   ☺ ○   😐 ○   ☹ ○

Writing Genre – Parts of an Explanatory Text

A Fill in the correct words from the word box.

| why animals hibernate | interesting fact | title |
| what hibernation means | how hibernation works |

Why Do Animals Hibernate?

Hibernation is when animals go into a deep sleep during the winter months and do not wake up until springtime. There are lots of animals that hibernate, including hedgehogs, bats, frogs, squirrels and insects.

In winter, it gets very cold and it is **difficult** for animals to find food. We all need food to live. It gives us the **energy** we use to breathe, eat, drink and even to think. It is easy for humans to find food in winter. All we need to do is go shopping. Animals must go into a deep sleep instead.

A hedgehog making a nest

To **prepare** for the deep sleep, they build up layers of fat under their skin. They do this by eating large amounts of food in autumn. Then, they find somewhere **suitable** to sleep. This might be in a ditch, beneath a pile of branches or even inside a cave. When they go to sleep, their body **temperature** drops, their heartbeat slows down and it is very hard to wake them. They save their energy by not running around, and **survive** on the fat stored under their skin instead of eating food. They sleep like this throughout the winter. Some animals wake up for a short time on warmer days and look for a snack that they may have hidden nearby.

Finally, the animals wake up in springtime when food becomes easier to find once again.

Did you know that some animals go into such a deep sleep that they may appear to be dead?

A squirrel eating lots of nuts

Strand: Writing Elements: Communicating LO 1; Understanding LO 5; Exploring and Using LO 8

Why Trees Drop Their Leaves 3

Phonics Game	/oa/ sound family – oa, o_e, ow	/ie/ sound family – ie, i_e, y, igh

A Before you begin the game, tick (✓) the sounds that you are able to read.

ee		ie		ow		ai		i_e		ay		y	
o_e		ea		oa		mp		ie		st		sh	

B Snakes and Ladders

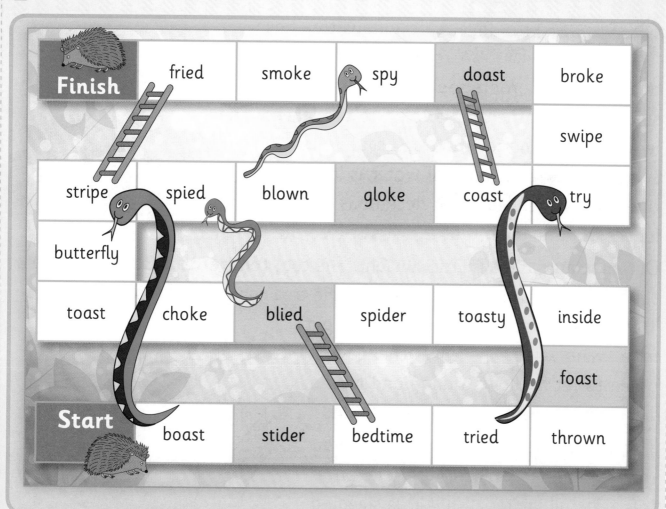

Try playing this at home again. All you need is a die and a set of counters.

Comprehension

Do you know what the **bold** words below mean? Can you explain them to your partner?

Look out for words from the /oa/ and /ie/ sound families in the explanation below.

Why Do Some Trees Drop Their Leaves?

A tree in autumn

There are three main types of tree in the world: palm trees, conifers and **deciduous** trees. Deciduous trees are special, because they drop their leaves in autumn.

A deciduous tree has roots, a trunk, branches and leaves. The roots soak up water from the soil. The water then **travels** up to the leaves. The leaves make food for the tree using water, air and sunlight. However, a lot of water is lost through tiny holes in the leaves. A deciduous tree drops its leaves in autumn so that it will **survive** the winter.

A tree in winter

During winter, there is little sunlight. The cold **temperatures** mean that the soil might be frozen and the roots of the tree cannot soak up much water.

The tree needs to drop its leaves to stop it from losing water. The leaves change from green to red, yellow, orange and brown. They slowly die and fall to the ground.

This allows the tree to sleep in the way that some animals hibernate. The bare tree rests all winter. While it is sleeping, it does not need as much food or water. In springtime, when the weather gets warmer, the tree starts to grow buds and leaves again.

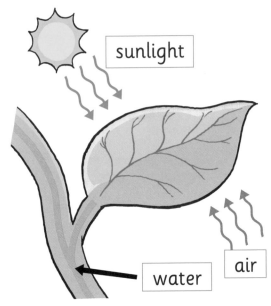

How a leaf makes food

Strand: Reading **Elements:** Communicating LO 1; Understanding LO 4, 5, 6

A In your copy, go investigate. 🔍

1. Name the three main types of tree in the world.

2. What type of tree drops its leaves?

3. When does this tree drop its leaves?

4. To what colours do the leaves change in autumn?

5. What three things does a leaf need to make food?

6. What do trees do during winter?

7. What does a deciduous tree start to grow in springtime?

B In your copy, give your opinion. 💭?

1. What do you think would happen if our winters were to become warmer and sunnier?

2. How are deciduous trees and animals that hibernate similar?

3. How are deciduous trees and animals that hibernate different?

4. Which is your favourite season of the year? Why?

C Vocabulary: Write the correct word. ✏️

		 I would love some.	
there	**their**	**would**	**wood**

1. The mouse ran over _____ .

2. _____ was no one home, so we left.

3. Is that _____ dog?

4. We get _____ from trees.

5. I _____ like to join the basketball team.

6. _____ you like some chocolate cake?

7. Can you take me _____ the shop later? **to / too**

8. Did you know that Harry has a dog _____ ? **to / too**

Phonics

| /oa/ sound family – oa, o_e, ow | /ie/ sound family – ie, i_e, y, igh |

You can spell the /oa/ sound using the following letters:

| soap | robe | bowl |

You can spell the /ie/ sound using the following letters:

| pie | nine | spy | right |

A Tick (✓) the real words and ✗ the nonsense words.

1. cied ✗
2. sky ✓
3. zail
4. narrow
5. blie
6. lied
7. choke
8. invite
9. cly
10. rainbow
11. bedtide
12. flashlight
13. snowflike
14. bright
15. outside
16. doaster
17. butterfly
18. funbide

B Write the correct word.

1. That boy ____ to tell lies. **likes / life**
2. My bedtime is at ____ o'clock every night. **nine / nose**
3. I hope we get no ____ tonight. **hose / homework**
4. I like to sleep on my soft ____. **pillow / moan**
5. Who took a ____ out of the pie? **moan / bite**
6. I ____ I can have a bowl of jelly! **hide / hope**
7. Mike will give you a ____ of his bike. **borrow / loan**
8. Mum ____ all night to get home on time. **drove / throw**
9. My grandad used to smoke a ____. **night / pipe**
10. I like to hide my dad's keys as a ____. **coat / joke**

Strand: Reading Element: Understanding LO 4, 5

Grammar – Verbs

Verbs are doing words. They tell us what is happening.

Examples: sit    paint   run

A Fill in the correct verb from the word box.

comes   fall   rake   gets   wear   grow

1. Autumn _____ after summer and before winter.

2. In autumn, the weather _____ chilly.

3. The leaves _____ from the trees.

4. People _____ jumpers and coats.

5. People _____ up leaves in their gardens.

6. Acorns _____ on an oak tree.

> These are signs of autumn.

B Ring the two verbs in each sentence.

1. In autumn, the leaves fall from the trees and drop to the ground.

2. Bats find a safe place to sleep for winter.

3. Squirrels collect nuts to eat during the long winter.

4. Some birds leave and fly away to a warmer country.

5. The hedgehog makes a nest to sleep in.

6. The days get shorter and the nights grow longer.

C Dictation: Listen to your teacher and write the sentences.

1. _____

2. _____

How did you do? 🙂 ⚪ 😐 ⚪ 🙁 ⚪

Writing Genre – Modelled and Shared Writing

A Complete the fact file.

Read each fact about the life-cycle of an oak tree. Rewrite it in the correct box in the fact file.

Facts About the Life-cycle of an Oak Tree

1. starts as an acorn
2. shoots grow upwards
3. acorn cracks open
4. roots grow down into soil
5. large tree that grows acorns
6. can grow 2,000 acorns every year
7. has a trunk, bark, branches, leaves and nuts called acorns

Fact File About the Life-cycle of an Oak Tree

What is an oak tree?	Parts/Description of an oak tree

How it grows	Interesting fact

B With your class, write an explanation of the life-cycle of an oak tree.

Strand: Writing Elements: Communicating LO 1; Understanding LO 5; Exploring and Using LO 6, 7

Was Count Dracula Real? 4

Phonics Game	/ue/ sound family – ue, u_e, ew	/ou/ sound family – ou, ow

A Before you begin the game, tick (✓) the sounds that you are able to read.

ou		oa		ue		ie		ew		ai		u_e	
ow		ea		ee		ew		br		mp		nt	

B Four in a row

1 smissue	**2** cloudy	**3** missue	**4** newspaper	**5** smissue	**6** showery
1 however	**2** frew	**3** screw	**4** county	**5** prune	**6** glound
1 plune	**2** flute	**3** plowder	**4** blue	**5** shoudy	**6** true
1 ground	**2** crown	**3** fluke	**4** druke	**5** chewy	**6** sound
1 threw	**2** glue	**3** srew	**4** outside	**5** round	**6** snume
1 powder	**2** flound	**3** include	**4** blowder	**5** flowery	**6** jewellery

Try playing this at home again. All you need is a die and a set of counters.

Comprehension

Do you know what the **bold** words below mean? Can you explain them to your partner?

Look out for words from the /ue/ and /ou/ sound families in the explanation below.

Was Count Dracula Real?

Count Dracula is the most famous vampire of all time. There are lots of books, cartoons, TV programmes and films about him. However, many people ask, "Did Dracula really exist? Did he really suck blood from his **victims**?"

Dracula – the most famous vampire

Bram Stoker

The novel 'Dracula' was written by an Irish **author** named Bram Stoker. Bram Stoker was born in Clontarf in Dublin and worked in Dublin Castle. He liked adventure stories and loved to write. It is said that he was very sick when he was small and spent a lot of time in bed. His mother told him stories and he loved scary tales **in particular**. When he was older, someone told him the story of a cruel prince named Dracula, who had lived in **Romania** many years ago. Bram Stoker wanted to find out if the story was true, so he read as much as he could about Dracula and a place called Transylvania. However, the real Dracula had never lived in Transylvania!

Prince Dracula lived over five hundred years ago in a big castle high up in the mountains in Romania. This was at a time when there were many wars. As he was a prince, he was powerful and had an army. It is said that he was very nasty and his army killed thousands of people very cruelly. There is no proof that he was a vampire, though. He probably would have been forgotten if Bram Stoker hadn't borrowed his name and **invented** his story!

Did you know that, today, hundreds of people visit Bran Castle in Transylvania? It is quite spooky, as it is high up in the mountains and covered in fog, but the real Prince Dracula never lived there!

Strand: Reading Elements: Communicating LO 1; Understanding LO 4, 5, 6

A In your copy, go investigate.

1. Who wrote the novel 'Dracula'?

2. Where was Bram Stoker born?

3. What did Bram Stoker enjoy doing?

4. Where did Bram Stoker work?

5. Where did the real Prince Dracula live?

6. Why did Prince Dracula have an army?

7. What did Prince Dracula do with his army?

8. Why have we not forgotten about Dracula?

B In your copy, give your opinion.

1. How do you think Bram Stoker felt when he heard the story of Dracula?

2. Where do you think Bram Stoker found stories about Dracula?

3. Do you think that his mother's stories caused Bram Stoker to enjoy scary tales? Give reasons for your answer.

4. Do you think that Dracula was real? Give reasons for your answer.

5. Can you think of another title for this reading piece?

6. If you could ask Bram Stoker two questions, what would they be?

C Vocabulary: Write the correct word.

 **be**	**bee**	**which**	**witch**

1. The _____ flew into the beehive.

2. I want to _____ a zookeeper when I grow up.

3. The _____ flew past on her broomstick.

4. I don't know _____ one is my favourite.

5. _____ one is your bike?

Phonics

/ue/ sound family	/ou/ sound family
– ue, u_e, ew	– ou, ow

A Look at the picture. Tick (✓) true or false for each sentence.

1. Sue is cleaning her hands on a towel.   True   False
2. A bag of flour has been spilled on the ground.   True   False
3. Outside, it is a cloudy day.   True   False
4. There is a pot of stew boiling on the stove.   True   False
5. There is a box of tissues on the couch.   True   False
6. It is June.   True   False
7. There are screws beside the the toolbox.   True   False
8. The child threw the clown on the ground.   True   False
9. The child is chewing a toy owl.   True   False
10. There is a vase of flowers on the windowsill.   True   False
11. There is a bowl of blueberries on the couch.   True   False
12. Yesterday's newspaper is on the ground.   True   False

B Write the correct word.

1. Andrew bought a bunch of _____ in the shop.
   queue / **flowers**

2. Sue has a _____ pet mouse in her house. **cow** / **cute**

3. The wind blew the dark _____ across the sky.
   clouds / **down**

Strand: Reading Element: Understanding LO 4, 5

Grammar – Alphabetical Order

If two or more words start with the same letter, look at the next letter in each word.

Example: sp**e**ll, sp**i**der

Look! The word 'spell' comes first, because it begins with sp**e**.

A Number each set of words in alphabetical order.

1. black   bat   broom

2. creepy   cloak   cat

3. fang   fright   fog

4. spider   shock   scary

B Ring the word that comes first in alphabetical order.

1. skull   (skeleton)   2. cobweb   coffin

3. monster   moon   4. shock   shadow

5. boo   bones   6. vanish   vampire

7. blood   black   8. treat   trick

C Number each set of words in alphabetical order.

1. cat   cauldron   cape

2. haunt   hat   Hallowe'en

3. wizard   wicked   witch

4. mask   magic   maze

D Dictation: Listen to your teacher and write the sentences.

1. _____

2. _____

How did you do? 🙂 ⬤ 😐 ⬤ ☹ ⬤

Writing Genre – Independent Writing

A Complete the fact file.

Read each fact about why we brush our teeth. Rewrite it in the correct box in the fact file. Can you research other interesting facts by yourself?

Facts About Why We Brush our Teeth

1. most foods have sugar, which sticks to our teeth
2. long ago, people used ashes from a fireplace to clean their teeth!
3. sugar eats away at our teeth
4. help us to chew and to talk
5. teeth are white, have a hard outer shell
6. teeth are important
7. are surrounded by gums

Fact File About Why We Brush our Teeth

What are teeth?	Parts/Description of teeth
Why we brush our teeth?	**Interesting fact**

B Write an explanation of why we brush our teeth by yourself. Use the fact file to help you.

C Look over your explanation again. Did you remember everything?

Strand: Writing Elements: Communicating LO 1; Understanding LO 5; Exploring and Using LO 6, 7

Minding Baby Elle

Phonics Game | /ool/ sound family – le | /u/ sound family – ou

A Before you begin the game, tick (✓) the sounds that you are able to read.

oa		le		igh		ou		ow		ue		ee	
ew		ck		le		ie		ou		a_e		ng	

B Roll and read.

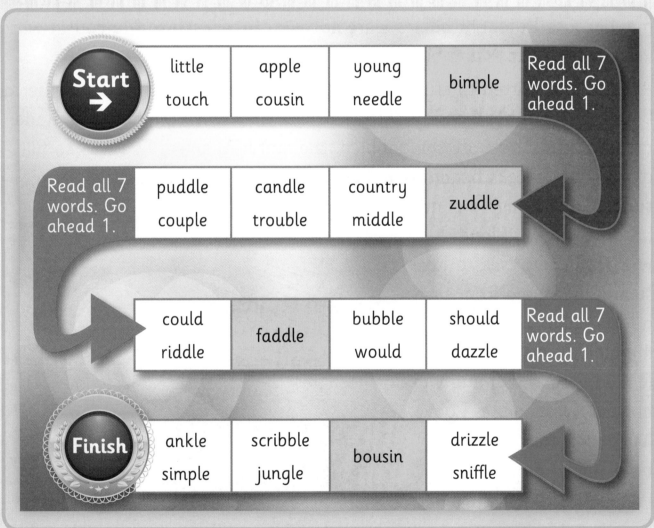

| Start → | little / touch | apple / cousin | young / needle | bimple | Read all 7 words. Go ahead 1. |

| Read all 7 words. Go ahead 1. | puddle / couple | candle / trouble | country / middle | zuddle |

| | could / riddle | faddle | bubble / would | should / dazzle | Read all 7 words. Go ahead 1. |

| Finish | ankle / simple | scribble / jungle | bousin | drizzle / sniffle |

Try playing this at home again. All you need is a die and a set of counters.

Strand: Reading Element: Understanding LO 4, 5

Comprehension

Do you know what the **bold** words below mean? Can you explain them to your partner?

Sometimes the letters **ou** make the /u/ sound. Look out for words with **ou** or **le** in the story below.

Minding Baby Elle

Last week, my **eldest** cousin and her new baby came to visit. My cousin said that she needed to go shopping and Mum thought it would be a great idea if we took care of baby Elle. It sounded like a terrible idea to me, because I thought babies were not very **interesting**. My cousin was very **grateful** to Mum, but nobody asked me.

At first, Elle started to cry. She made a lot of noise until Mum gave her a bottle. She **gobbled** and gobbled her milk. It was very funny and made me **chuckle**. The more she gobbled, the more I giggled! Elle was so full of milk, her cheeks began to wobble and her face turned purple! Then,

suddenly, she gave a huge burp. It was very loud. I was really surprised to hear such a big sound from such a little baby. This made me giggle even more. Elle looked very happy and was not purple anymore. I gave her a little tickle and we both smiled again.

Later on, I showed her a puzzle and I showed her how to juggle. She is still too young to do it by herself, but she liked to watch me. When she is bigger, I will teach her.

I still think babies can be smelly sometimes, but they are good fun. I can't wait until Elle comes to visit again.

Strand: Reading Elements: Communicating LO 1; Understanding LO 4, 5, 6

A In your copy, go investigate. 🔍

1. When did the boy's cousin come to visit?

2. What did his cousin need to do?

3. How did his cousin feel when Mum offered to babysit?

4. How did Mum stop Elle from crying?

5. What will the boy do when Elle is older?

6. Why did the boy think it was a terrible idea to mind Elle?

7. How does the boy feel about minding Elle again?

B In your copy, give your opinion. 💭

1. Why do you think Mum thought it would be a good idea to mind Elle?

2. How do you think the boy felt when no one asked him if he wanted to mind Elle?

3. Why do you think Elle started crying?

4. How do you think the boy felt when Elle went home?

5. Do you like minding babies? Why/Why not?

C Vocabulary: Match each word to its opposite. ✏️

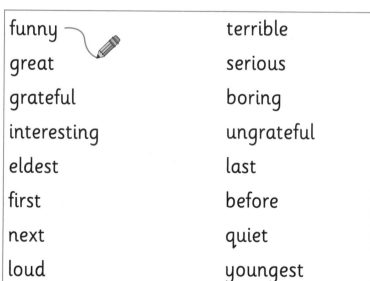

funny	terrible
great	serious
grateful	boring
interesting	ungrateful
eldest	last
first	before
next	quiet
loud	youngest

D Oral language 💬

Make a list of time words in the story. Can you think of any more?

Then, in pairs, take it in turns to retell the story 'Minding Baby Elle'.

Be sure to tell it in the correct order and don't forget your time words.

Strand: Reading Elements: Understanding LO 6; Exploring and Using LO 8, 9
Strand: Oral Language Element: Exploring and Using LO 11

27

Phonics | /ool/ sound family – le | /u/ sound family – ou

A Look at each picture. Tick (✓) the correct word.

paddle		jungle		cuddle	
puddle	✓	jiggle		candle	
pebble		juggle		crackle	
ankle		puzzle		cuddle	
apple		poodle		cackle	
able		pimple		chuckle	
trundle		bubble		sparkle	
tickle		bottle		sprinkle	
tackle		bumble		scribble	
huddle		middle		rumble	
handle		muddle		ramble	
handlebars		meddle		rattle	

B Read each sentence and cross out the incorrect word.

1. Tigers and snakes live in the jungle south.

2. Did you get plate enough apple pie to eat?

3. Yesterday, I did a loud jig-saw puzzle with my cousin Kevin.

4. Last night, Dad could not open the car door. The handle drew was stuck.

5. Next weekend, we are going to the country to coach visit my cousin.

6. Dad said we could not go out to play, as it was raincoat starting to drizzle.

7. Mum gave the young baby a bottle and a little rattle tickle to play with.

8. That young boy got into trouble when he threw a bubbly pebble at a window.

Strand: Reading **Element:** Understanding LO 4, 5, 6

Grammar – Past Tense Verbs – 'ed

The 1:1:1 Rule

If a word has:	Double the f...
one **syllable**	**Examples:**
one **vowel**	nod → no...
one final **consonant**	fit → fitt...

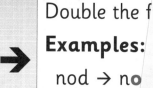

Writing Genre

A Fix the recou...
Read the parts
could also p...

Unit 5 | Recount 1

A Ring the correct spelling of each f...

clapped claped	paintted painted	waited waitted	slipped sliped	skiped skipped

beeped beepped	huged hugged	counted countted	droped dropped	waged wagged

B Complete each sentence in the past tense by changing the verb in brackets.

1. Last summer, I _____ (pack) my own bag for our holidays.

2. A few days ago, Matilda _____ (hum) a tune for us.

3. Last week, we _____ (watch) a very scary film on TV.

4. On Friday, Panya and I _____ (play) a game.

5. A month ago, my sister _____ (rub) shampoo in her eyes.

C Dictation: Listen to your teacher and write the sentences.

1. _____

2. _____

How did you do? 🙂 ⚪ 😐 ⚪ ☹️ ⚪

...nt. ✏️

...s of the story and number them in the correct order. (You
...hotocopy this page, cut it up and put it in order with a partner.)

	At first, Elle started to cry. She made a lot of noise until Mum gave her a bottle.	
	Last week, my eldest cousin and her new baby came to visit.	
	Elle was so full of milk, her cheeks began to wobble and her face turned purple! Then, suddenly, she gave a huge burp.	
	Later on, I showed her a puzzle and I showed her how to juggle.	
1	**Minding Baby Elle**	
	My cousin said that she needed to go shopping and Mum thought it would be a great idea if we took care of baby Elle.	
	She gobbled and gobbled her milk.	

B In pairs, find the parts of the recount above.

1. Can you find the title?

2. Can you find the when, who, what, where and why?

3. How many events can you find?

4. Can you think of another clever ending?

TVFlicks.com 6

Phonics Game /sh/ sound family – sion, tion

A Before you begin the game, tick (✓) the sounds that you are able to read. ✏

ow		tion		le		sion		ew		ou		sion	
igh		nk		tion		o_e		lt		sion		u_e	

B A spin and a roll

We all say nonsense words!

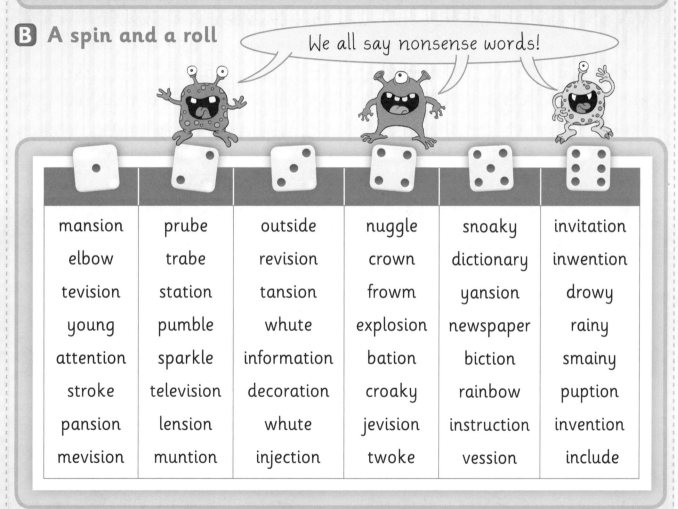

mansion	prube	outside	nuggle	snoaky	invitation
elbow	trabe	revision	crown	dictionary	inwention
tevision	station	tansion	frowm	yansion	drowy
young	pumble	whute	explosion	newspaper	rainy
attention	sparkle	information	bation	biction	smainy
stroke	television	decoration	croaky	rainbow	puption
pansion	lension	whute	jevision	instruction	invention
mevision	muntion	injection	twoke	vession	include

Try playing this with two players at home. Simply rub out the words you have ringed in class. This time, Player One can underline words and Player Two can ring them. Whoever fills a column first wins!

Comprehension

Do you know what the **bold** words below mean? Can you explain them to your partner?

Look out for words with sion or tion in the menu below.

TVFlicks.com

Account Login:

Username: **Password:**

Click on what you would like to watch now.

Children's films

Double Trouble

A film about twins who get up to lots of terrible tricks

The Jungle Book

A film about a little boy living in the jungle with lots of animal friends

The Little Poodle

A brilliant film packed with lots of traps and a **rescue mission** for a little **poodle**

Films

Mission Impossible

A film about a man sent on a **mission** to hunt down a bank robber

The Haunted Mansion

A scary film about a boy trick-or-treating and visiting a haunted house

The Big Explosion

An exciting film about a fireman saving the lives of lots of people

Documentaries

Bake Time

A **documentary** showing how to make a yummy apple pie

The Big Bumble

A documentary about the bumblebee – find out where it lives and more!

The Problem with Pollution

A documentary explaining how **pollution** is **harming** the planet and its **wildlife**

Irish Music

A documentary that looks at **traditional** Irish music and the fiddle

Your Home

A documentary showing how you can build your own home or a new **extension**

Strand: Reading **Elements:** Communicating LO 1; Understanding 4, 5, 6

A In your copy, go investigate.

1. How many children's films are there?

2. What is the name of the film about twins?

3. What is the name of the scary film?

4. If you were to watch 'Bake Time', what could you learn to do?

5. What can you find out from the documentary about the bumblebee?

6. If you were building a new extension, what might you like to watch?

7. If you wanted to hear fiddle-playing, what might you like to watch?

B In your copy, give your opinion.

1. Would you like to watch 'The Big Bumble'? Why/Why not?

2. Which documentary would you like to watch? Why?

3. Which film would you like to watch? Why?

4. What do you think 'The Little Poodle' is about?

5. What would you recommend for a little child to watch?

6. What would you recommend for a grown-up to watch? Why?

C Vocabulary: Match each word to its meaning.

exciting	something that is not interesting
funny	something that gives you a fright
scary	something that makes you chuckle
boring	something that is very interesting or fun

D Vocabulary: Ring the word with a similar meaning.

1. funny: **sad / silly**

2. boring: **dull / amazing**

3. scary: **creepy / happy**

4. exciting: **boring / amazing**

Phonics /sh/ sound family – sion, tion

A Look at each picture. Tick (✓) the correct word.

lotion ✓
location
action

decoration
dictionary
television

instruction
invitation
injection

caution
confession
confusion

permission
portion
pension

pollution
protection
permission

caution
station
section

conversation
collection
collision

B Read each sentence and cross out the incorrect word.

1. My birthday was a very sweet happy occasion.
2. It is caution important to wear sun lotion in the summer.
3. I ask questions action when I am confused in class.
4. You must ask your parents can for permission to go out and play.

C Follow the instruction or write the answer.

1. What colour is the flat screen television?
2. Only answer the subtraction sum. $4 + 4 =$ $3 - 1 =$
3. What is the last letter in the dictionary?
4. Draw a capital letter on the biggest bottle of sun lotion.

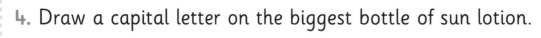

Strand: Reading Element: Understanding LO 4, 5, 6

Grammar – Past Tense Irregul[...]

Some verbs do not take **'ed'** in the past ten[...]
verbs. We must learn these verbs off by hea[...]

Examples: swim – On Monday, I **swam**[...]

drink – This morning, I **dran**[...]

A Match each verb to its past tense.

fall	ate
say	said
go	made
eat	fell
make	went

have	[...]
get	[...]
ride	had
hide	got
do	hid

B Write the correct verb to complete each sentence.

1. Last summer, I _____ to the lake. **go / went / gone**

2. Yesterday, I _____ a new fiddle. **got / get / given**

3. Last week, I _____ pebbles in the puddle. **thrown / threw**

4. Yesterday, we _____ songs in school. **sang / sing / song**

5. Last night, I _____ the baby a rattle. **get / give / gave**

6. A year ago, I _____ to juggle three balls. **learned / learn**

7. Last night, Dad _____ me a cuddle. **gave / give**

8. Two days ago, I _____ very sick. **were / was / is**

9. Last year, Marcus _____ a stray kitten. **found / find**

10. Yesterday morning, Ayo _____ his wallet. **lose / lost**

C Dictation: Listen to your teacher and write the sentences.

1. _____

2. _____

How did you do?

nt.

a recount of something that happened in school. It could be
that happened during P.E., mathematics, a trip or a visit.

Recount Planner

Title:

When	Who	What

Event 1	Event 2	Event 3

A clever ending (Tip: Don't rush!)

Ring some time words to help you.

this week   today   this morning   on Tuesday   first   next
then   after that   soon   later on   finally   at last

B With your class, write the recount.

Rudolph's Diary

Phonics Game	/ai/ sound family – ei, eigh	/f/ sound family – ph

A Before you begin the game, tick (✓) the sounds that you are able to read.

ph		sion		eigh		le		tion		ei		ou	
eigh		ue		ie		nk		ph		ou		ai	

B Snakes and Ladders

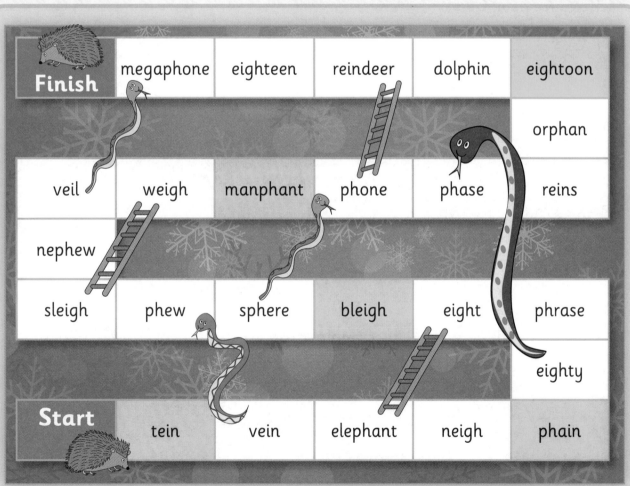

Finish — megaphone — eighteen — reindeer — dolphin — eightoon

orphan

veil — weigh — manphant — phone — phase — reins

nephew

sleigh — phew — sphere — bleigh — eight — phrase

eighty

Start — tein — vein — elephant — neigh — phain

Try playing this at home again. All you need is a die and a set of counters.

Comprehension

Do you know what the **bold** words below mean?
Can you explain them to your partner?

Sometimes the letters **ei** and **eigh** make the /ai/ sound.
Look out for words with **ei**, **eigh** or **ph** in the diary below.

Rudolph's Diary

Monday
Today wasn't good. First of all, Dasher lay in his stable all day, as he is lame. Before long, Frosty the elf was running around like mad. He's very worried.

Tuesday
I thought poor Dasher would be better this morning, but he is far worse. Frosty has been getting more **bothered** by the minute.

Wednesday
This morning, Frosty went crazy. He said that Santa cannot fly his sleigh without Dasher.
There is no way he can do it with just eight of us. He says that Christmas will have to be **put on hold** this year. What will we do?

Thursday
Today, Frosty told Dasher that he is like a big, lazy elephant. He said, "I need nine reindeer for the sleigh to **travel** as fast as a train and fly like an aeroplane."

Friday
After lunch, I heard Frosty **complaining** to the reindeer vet on the phone. He said that Dasher is going through a **phase** and is just a big, lazy lump. He thought he might get a **megaphone** and roar in Dasher's ear. That might make him jump up out of his stable!

Saturday
Phew! On the eve of Christmas Eve, Dasher was on the mend.
Mrs Claus made him some Christmas pudding. It's his favourite.

Sunday
It's Christmas Eve and we have packed up the sleigh. It is time to be on our merry way. I love Christmas Eve. It's the best night of the year!

Strand: Reading Elements: Communicating LO 1; Understanding LO 4, 5, 6

A In your copy, go investigate.

1. Who wrote this diary?

2. Which elf looks after the reindeer?

3. How would you describe this elf?

4. Where did Dasher lie all day?

5. How many reindeer does Santa need to fly his sleigh?

6. Who did Frosty the elf call?

7. What did Mrs Claus make Dasher to eat?

B In your copy, give your opinion.

1. Do you think Dasher was a lazy lump? Why?

2. Why do you think Frosty the elf called Dasher a lazy lump?

3. Why was Frosty the elf so bothered that Dasher was unwell?

4. What could Frosty or Santa have done if Dasher wasn't feeling better?

5. Do you think they would have put Christmas on hold? Why/Why not?

6. Who do you think might have helped to pack up the sleigh?

7. Why do you think Rudolph likes Christmas Eve so much?

C Vocabulary: Ring the odd one out in each set.

1. chocolate	cake	sweets	tree
2. bells	snowman	hat	scarf
3. tree	fairy lights	cake	decorations
4. Santa	holly	sleigh	reindeer
5. present	ribbon	bow	ruler
6. card	stocking	letter	present

Strand: Reading Elements: Understanding LO 6; Exploring and Using LO 8, 9

Phonics /ai/ sound family – ei, eigh | /f/ sound family – ph

You can spell the /ai/ sound using the following letters:

| snail | cake | May | reindeer | sleigh |

You can spell the /f/ sound using the following letters:

| leaf | Philip |

A Tick (✓) the real words and ✗ the nonsense words.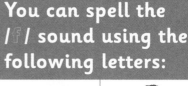

1. phone ✓
2. tein ✗
3. phew
4. vein
5. beim
6. eight
7. phonics
8. phane
9. eighth
10. phruse
11. weigh
12. phunics
13. dolphin
14. alphabet
15. fleigh

B Fill in the correct word from the word box.

| dolphin | weigh | eighty | alphabet | orphan |
| sleigh | phonics | elephant | neighbour | reindeer |

1. An _____ has no parents.
2. An _____ is a big mammal with a trunk and tusks.
3. How much does a bag of flour _____?
4. My _____ lives next door to us.
5. You use a _____ to travel over snow.
6. A _____ is an animal like a small whale.
7. My little sister is learning to sing the _____.
8. My granny will be _____ on her next birthday.
9. Learning about sounds can also be called _____.
10. _____ use their hooves to dig for food in the snow.

Strand: Reading Element: Understanding LO 4, 5, 6

Grammar – Nouns

Nouns are naming words. They tell us the name of:

 a person   a place   an animal   a thing

A Write three nouns for each of the following.

Presents you give at Christmas	Food you eat at Christmas	Places you visit at Christmas	People you see at Christmas
1.	1.	1.	1.
2.	2.	2.	2.
3.	3.	3.	3.

B Ring the nouns in each sentence.

1. Yesterday, my grandma went to church.

2. On Wednesday, my dad posted all of our Christmas cards.

3. I gave my grandad a big hug when he gave me a present.

4. I hope I get sweets and chocolates in my stocking.

5. The elf jumped up and down on Santa's sack.

6. I pulled a Christmas cracker with my cousin Ben.

7. We will visit my cousins in Cork over Christmas.

8. We put decorations and fairy lights on our Christmas tree.

9. Santa has nine reindeer to pull his sleigh.

C Dictation: Listen to your teacher and write the sentences.

1. _____

2. _____

How did you do? 🙂◯ 😐◯ 🙁◯

Writing Genre – Independent Writing

A Plan a recount.

In pairs, pick and plan one of these recounts:

1. Our Christmas Show **2.** Visiting Santa **3.** Making Christmas Art

Recount Planner

Title:

When	Who	What
Event 1	**Event 2**	**Event 3**

A clever ending (Tip: Don't rush!)

Ring some time words to help you.

this week	today	this morning	on Tuesday	first	next
then	after that	soon	later on	finally	at last

B Write the recount by yourself. Include a title and three events. Don't forget to use time words.

C Look over your recount again. Did you remember everything?

Strand: **Writing Elements:** Communicating LO 1, 2; Exploring and Using LO 6, 7

Revision and Assessment 8

Revision: Grammar and Phonics

Day 1

1. **Ring the word that does not need a capital letter.**

   (a) Aoife   Molly   Girl   Hannah

   (b) Spain   September   Snake

2. **Number each set in alphabetical order.**

   (a) bike ▢   blocks ▢   ball ▢

   (b) ship ▢   swing ▢   slide ▢

3. **Is the underlined word a noun or a verb?**

   (a) Dad put the paint in the <u>shed</u>.

   Noun ▢   Verb ▢

   (b) Mum <u>drove</u> to work in her new car.

   Noun ▢   Verb ▢

4. **Ring the correct spelling for each verb.**

   (a) I slipped / sliped on the ice.

   (b) I sharred / shared my toys.

5. **Tick the real words.**

   tansion ▢   information ▢

   noodle ▢   mittle ▢

   dolphin ▢   veigh ▢

   reindeer ▢   cousin ▢

Day 2

1. **Ring the word that does not need a capital letter.**

   (a) Tomas   Ten   Tom   Tuesday

   (b) Cavan   Cara   Cat   Colm

2. **Number each set in alphabetical order.**

   (a) doll ▢   dice ▢   drum ▢

   (b) truck ▢   teddy ▢   toy ▢

3. **Is the underlined word a noun or a verb?**

   (a) Ryan <u>shouted</u> at Alex.

   Noun ▢   Verb ▢

   (b) Would you like a <u>sweet</u>?

   Noun ▢   Verb ▢

4. **Ring the correct spelling for each verb.**

   (a) Rory invitted / invited me to his party.

   (b) The dog wagged / waged its tail.

5. **Tick the real words.**

   enough ▢   pham ▢

   jollision ▢   mansion ▢

   kuggle ▢   glight ▢

   continue ▢   slousin ▢

43

Day 3

1. **Ring the words that need a capital letter.**

   (a) dad went to see his aunt lily today.

   (b) the months of winter are november, december and january.

2. **Number each set in alphabetical order.**

   (a) bat   ball   bike

   (b) puzzle   pool   puppet

3. **Ring two nouns in each sentence.**

   (a) My favourite dessert is pie.

   (b) We went to Kerry and Cork.

4. **Ring the correct spelling for each verb.**

   (a) Dad dropped / droped a glass.

   (b) I playyed / played with Layla.

5. **Tick the real words.**

   ziddle   television

   touch   weigh

   bulture   phobbo

   munsion   temperature

Day 4

1. **Ring the words that need a capital letter.**

   (a) do you play basketball on saturday and wednesday?

   (b) my sister and i like riding our bikes.

2. **Number each set in alphabetical order.**

   (a) skates   scooter   spade

   (b) paint   pens   pots

3. **Ring two nouns in each sentence.**

   (a) I went to the shop and got a book.

   (b) Harry loves to play football.

4. **Ring the correct spelling for each verb.**

   (a) We visitted / visited Grandad.

   (b) My brother slammed / slamed the door.

5. **Tick the real words.**

   fraction   bumble

   zeil   orphem

   wousin   didsty

   elephant   injection

Assessment: Phonics

A Follow the instruction or write the answer.

1. Ring the first day of the week.	**Monday Tuesday** Wednesday **Thursday** Friday **Saturday** Sunday
2. What colour is the smallest candle?	
3. Underline the elephant in the middle.	
4. Draw some decorations on the green tree in the snow.	
5. Put a question mark at the end of the sentence.	**What would you like for Christmas**
6. What is the first letter of the alphabet?	
7. Cross out all of the purple shapes.	
8. Write your name on the birthday invitation.	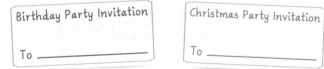
9. Write the number 8 above the eight yellow dots.	
10. Draw a circle around the last reindeer.	

Assessment: Comprehension

Rover Saves Christmas

They were in the **barn** behind Santa's house and workshop. Outside, elves on **snowmobiles** and sledges pulled by husky dogs **charged** across the yard. They were bringing sacks full of just-made presents to all of the sleighs lined up in a long, long row. The reindeer were **harnessed** and very excited. This was their big night.

But, inside the barn, it was very quiet. Santa was wearing a brand-new suit. It was red, of course, a beautiful bright red, because it was so new. He had loved the old suit – the most **famous** suit in the world – but it had ripped when he was bending over to put on his boots.

"You need a new suit," said Mrs Claus as she looked at Santa's underpants sticking out of the big hole at the back of his trousers.

"I need a new bum," Santa laughed. "This one's too big."

But Santa wasn't laughing now. The suit was supposed to make anyone who wore it or saw it happy, but it wasn't working.

Santa looked sad and worried.

(From 'Rover Saves Christmas' by Roddy Doyle)

Assessment: Comprehension and Vocabulary

A In your copy, go investigate.

1. What were pulling the sledges?

2. Why were the reindeer excited?

3. What were in the sacks?

4. Who told Santa that he needed a new suit?

5. How had Santa ripped his suit?

6. How was Santa feeling?

B In your copy, give your opinion.

1. Why do you think Santa was worried?

2. Where do you think Santa might get a new suit at the last minute?

3. What do you think happened next?

C Vocabulary: Write the correct word. ✏️

1. Daisy said that she will ⬚ here soon. **be / bee**

2. Can you put the box over ⬚ , please? **there / their**

3. We got ⬚ little puppies last week. **to / two / too**

4. ⬚ you pass me the paint, please? **would / wood**

5. Aoife dressed up as a ⬚ for Hallowe'en. **which / witch**

6. It was cold, so they put on ⬚ coats. **there / their**

7. My little sister will go to ⬚ Santa. **see / sea**

8. I ate ⬚ many sweets at the party. **to / two / too**

9. ⬚ one do you prefer? **which / witch**

10. Teacher told us ⬚ take out our books. **to / two / too**

Assessment: Grammar

A Ring the words that do not need a capital letter.

1. Anna   Spain   Monday   Dog
2. Apple   Sunday   Belfast   Kate
3. Jack   Kerry   Saturday   Six
4. December   Football   Arjun   Cork

B Rewrite each set of words in alphabetical order.

1. tree, present, star   _____ , _____ , _____

2. decorations, lights, bells   _____ , _____ , _____

3. toy, tree, tinsel   _____ , _____ , _____

4. snow, Santa, scarf   _____ , _____ , _____

C Underline one or more verbs in each sentence.

1. I hung up my stocking by the fireplace.

2. My mum sends Christmas cards in the post.

3. We put up our tree and hung up our decorations.

4. We went into town and visited Santa.

D Is the underlined word a verb? Tick (✓) yes or no.

1. Hannah <u>loves</u> to bake buns.   Yes   No

2. I went shopping with my dad <u>yesterday</u>.   Yes   No

3. On Saturday, I <u>always</u> go to football training.   Yes   No

4. My pet cat <u>drinks</u> milk.   Yes   No

E Tick (✓) if the underlined word is spelled correctly.

1. My sister <u>grabbed</u> my hair.   2. I <u>visited</u> my friend Chin.

3. I <u>huged</u> my granny.   4. We <u>watcheed</u> television.

5. He <u>slammed</u> the door.   6. The dog <u>waged</u> its tail.

7. We <u>played</u> football.   8. I <u>hopped</u> all the way home.

Strand: Writing
Element: Understanding LO 3, 4, 5

How did you do?   ○   😐 ○   ○

The Polar Bear

| Phonics Game | Soft c | /au/ sound family – au, al, aw |

A Before you begin the game, tick (✓) the sounds that you are able to read.

ear		aw		le		igh		au		ea		i_e	
air		ph		sion		eigh		al		ear		au	

B Four in a row

1	2	3	4	5	6
author	fence	rawn	ice	dace	Paul
race	tice	crawl	pencil	sleepwalk	raul
smence	walking	pawm	chalk	vaunch	bear
wear	space	face	tace	nice	haunt
small	dice	swall	seesaw	circus	bawn
jalking	paunt	autumn	bault	talking	tear

Try playing this at home again. All you need is a die and a set of counters.

Strand: Reading Element: Understanding LO 4, 5

49

Comprehension

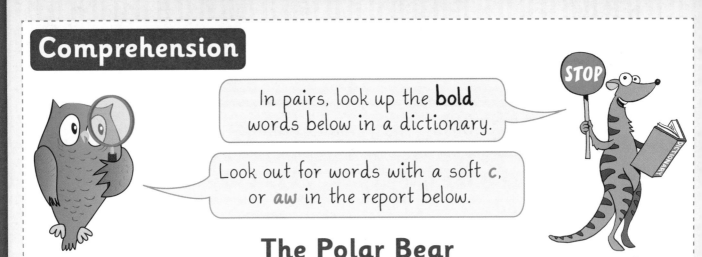

In pairs, look up the **bold** words below in a dictionary.

Look out for words with a soft **c**, or **aw** in the report below.

The Polar Bear

What is it?

The polar bear is a **mammal**. It is the biggest bear in the world.

What does it look like?

It has thick, white fur, which keeps it warm in the freezing cold. It has long claws on its paws, which help it to catch fish.

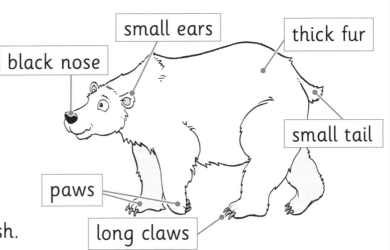

small ears

thick fur

black nose

small tail

paws

long claws

Where does it live?

It lives in the **Arctic**. The Artic is the most northern place on the planet. It is a very cold place.

What does it eat?

It mainly eats seals. Sometimes it eats other food such as walruses, **beached** whales and fish. In winter, the sea is frozen over like a sheet of ice. Seals swim below the ice, but when they find a hole in the ice, they pop up to breathe. The polar bear looks for these breathing holes. It has an excellent sense of smell and can find breathing holes very easily. When it finds one, it lies in wait nearby. As soon as it sees a seal **appear**, it jumps and **attacks** it.

Did you know?

Many people live in the Arctic and sometimes polar bears can **stray** into towns to find food. They also visit rubbish dumps, where they might get **poisoned** or **injured**.

A In your copy, go investigate.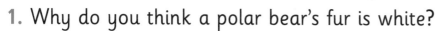

1. Where does the polar bear live?

2. Which is bigger, the polar bear or the brown bear?

3. What does the polar bear eat most of the time?

4. What other animals does the polar bear eat?

5. How does a polar bear keep warm?

6. Where do polar bears sometimes stray to look for food?

B In your copy, give your opinion.

1. Why do you think a polar bear's fur is white?

2. Why do you think polar bears sometimes visit rubbish dumps?

3. Do you think polar bears might become extinct? Why?

4. Polar bears are sometimes known as 'sea bears'. Can you guess why?

C Vocabulary: Ring the correct word.

1. The word 'thick' means: **thin / wide / skinny**

2. The word 'biggest' means: **massive / tiny / little**

3. The word 'cold' means: **warm / chilly / hot**

4. The word 'frozen' means: **warm / cool / icy**

5. The word 'excellent' means: **poor / great / fail**

6. The word 'stray' means: **roam / walk / dog**

7. The word 'injured' means: **better / hurt / unhappy**

Phonics Soft c | /au/ sound family – au, al, aw

When the vowel e or i, or the letter y follows c, this makes a /ss/ sound.

mice	pencil

A Read the clues and fill in the crossword.

circle   mice   rice   city   circus   ice   space   cinema   necklace

Across

1. The plural of 'mouse'

2. The planets and stars are found here.

3. Jewellery worn around the neck

4. This is frozen water.

Down

5. A round, flat shape

6. A place where you watch a film

7. Food that you eat with curry

8. A big, very important town

9. A show held in a tent

B Follow the instructions.

1.	Ring the tallest pencil.	
2.	Draw a circle around the princess.	
3.	Match the witch to her cauldron.	

Grammar – Adjectives 1

Adjectives are describing words. They tell us more about a noun.
Example: The **brown** bear is a **big** animal.

A Ring the best adjective for each sentence.

1. Paul sat on the **hot / silly / small** chair.

2. I saw a **scary / soft / sweet** film at the cinema.

3. We had some **chocolate / black / spicy** curry for dinner.

4. Our dog needs a haircut. He is very **filthy / hairy / old**.

5. It was freezing last night and the roads were very **icy / wet / fast**.

B Is the underlined word an adjective? Tick (✓) yes or no.

1. The <u>naughty</u> boy hit the old car.   Yes   No

2. My big brother is very <u>tall</u>.   Yes   No

3. Our black <u>cat</u> hurt her little paw yesterday.   Yes   No

4. The little baby likes to <u>crawl</u> on the nice rug.   Yes   No

5. Amber won an <u>amazing</u> prize in the competition.   Yes   No

C Write two adjectives for each noun.

cold	fresh	delicious	yummy	funny	warm	scary
old	happy	filthy	good	silly	mad	creamy

1.   mad   ,   hairy   dog   2. _____ , _____ film

3. _____ , _____ clown   4. _____ , _____ ice-cream

D Dictation: Listen to your teacher and write the sentences.

1. _____

2. _____

How did you do? ☺ ◯   😐 ◯   ☹ ◯

Writing Genre – Modelled and Shared Writing

A **Complete the fact file.**

Read each fact about seals. Rewrite it in the correct box in the fact file.

Facts About Seals

1. mammals
2. four flippers
3. fat under skin called blubber
4. fur is slick, helps them glide through water
5. live in the Arctic and Antarctic
6. fur is thick, helps keep them warm
7. eat fish, squid, shellfish, seabirds

Fact File About Seals

What are they?

Where do they live?

What do they look like?

What do they eat?

B **With your class, write a report on seals.**

Strand: Writing Elements: Communicating LO 1; Understanding LO 5; Exploring and Using LO 6, 7

Celebrating Chinese New Year

Phonics Game | /ee/ sound family – ey, ie | Silent w

A Before you begin the game, tick (✓) the sounds that you are able to read.

ee	ck	ie	ph	ear	aw	le
air	wr	ey	tion	ea	ear	ey

B Snakes and Ladders

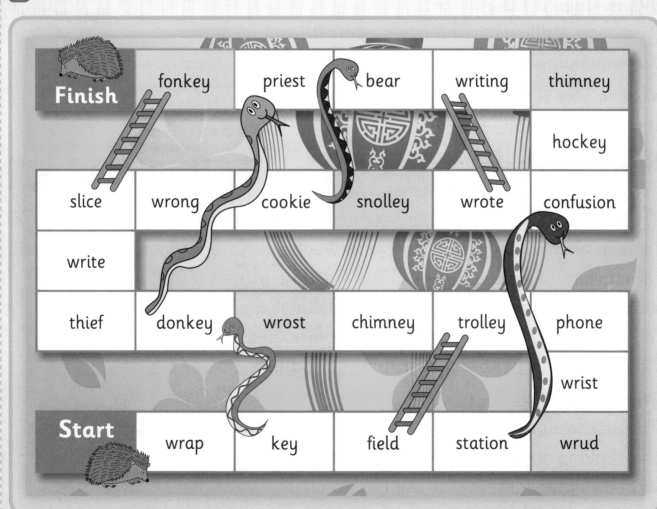

Finish

fonkey · priest · bear · writing · thimney

hockey

slice · wrong · cookie · snolley · wrote · confusion

write

thief · donkey · wrost · chimney · trolley · phone

wrist

Start · wrap · key · field · station · wrud

Try playing this at home again. All you need is a die and a set of counters.

Comprehension

In pairs, look up the **bold** words below in a dictionary.

Sometimes the letters **ie** make the /ee/ sound. Look out for words with **ie** or a silent **w** in the report below.

Celebrating Chinese New Year

What is it?

Chinese New Year is a very special **celebration** in China. It is a time when people wish for good luck and **peace**.

When does it take place?

It falls on a different date every year. It lasts for fifteen days, making it the longest celebration in China.

Where else is it celebrated?

It is celebrated all over the world.

How do people celebrate?

People spring-clean their homes and hang up decorations. They write poems on red banners and hang them from their doors and windows. They also wear red clothes. Families come together for a special dinner. They eat **dumplings** and the children eat **candied** crab apples on sticks. The children are given red envelopes full of money instead of wrapped presents. Red is a very special colour. Chinese people believe that it brings good luck.

The Lantern Festival

The celebration ends with the Lantern **Festival**. Lanterns are hung from trees, along streets and in the doorways of shops and offices. Riddles are written on the lanterns for children to guess. Everywhere is decorated with lanterns of different sizes and in the streets there is music and dancing.

Fortune cookies

If you visit China, you will not find fortune cookies there, but you can find them in Chinese restaurants in most other countries!

A In your copy, go investigate.

1. For how long does Chinese New Year last?

2. How do people get their homes ready?

3. What do people write on red banners?

4. What gifts are children given?

5. What treats do children eat?

6. Where are lanterns hung?

7. What do Chinese people believe that the colour red brings?

B In your copy, give your opinion.

1. When do you hang decorations in your home?

2. For your birthday, would you prefer an envelope of money or a gift? Why?

3. What other celebrations involve families coming together for a meal?

4. In Ireland, do we have a symbol of good luck? What is it?

5. Can you think of a riddle for a Chinese lantern?

C Vocabulary: Ring the odd one out in each set.

1. riddles	puzzle	game	homework
2. cry	sing	dancing	music
3. present	card	song	gift
4. decorations	lanterns	dinner	banners
5. rat	cake	tiger	rabbit

Phonics | /ee/ sound family – ey, ie | Silent w

You can spell the /ee/ sound using the following letters:					Sometimes the w is silent.		
wheel	beak	baby	monkey	movie	wrap	write	wrong

A Follow the instruction or write the answer.

1. Ring the tallest sword.

2. The _____ is eating a brownie.

3. Join the man to his briefcase.

4. Ring the boy who is doing a wheelie.

5. How many wrappers can you see?

B Ring the correct word in each set. In your copy, write a sentence for each of the ringed words.

1. toalie	goalie	moalie	poalie
2. mield	thield	mield	field
3. chimney	thimney	glimney	trimney
4. solley	trolley	blolley	tolley
5. wraim	wrast	wrost	wrist
6. wrine	wrete	wrote	wraist
7. wrostle	wrestle	wrastle	wristle

Don't forget to use a capital letter and a full stop.

Strand: Reading Element: Understanding LO 4, 5, 6

Grammar – Adjectives 2

A Fill in the best adjective from the word box.

wrong	small	long	yummy

1. A wren is a very _____ bird.
2. Zula loves to eat _____ chocolate-chip cookies.
3. Charlie will write a _____ letter to his pen pal.
4. The _____ dog was running around the park barking.
5. In my spelling test, I got three spellings _____ .

B Write the opposite of each adjective.

happy	hot	first	rich	brave	big	black	full	dry

1. white: _____
2. little: _____
3. empty: _____
4. poor: _____
5. cold: _____
6. sad: _____
7. afraid: _____
8. wet: _____
9. last: _____

C Sort the words into nouns, verbs and adjectives.

Words Used in Animal Reports

birds	warm	hairy	live	wet	plants	eat	hunt	food

Nouns	Verbs	Adjectives
birds		

D Dictation: Listen to your teacher and write the sentences.

1. _____
2. _____

How did you do? ☺ ○ 😐 ○ ☹ ○

Writing Genre – Independent Writing

A Complete the fact file.

Read each fact about the walrus. Rewrite it in the correct box in the fact file.

Facts About the Walrus

1. eats clams
2. found in Arctic Circle
3. big mammal
4. lots of blubber under skin
5. turns pink when older
6. wrinkled brown or grey skin
7. flippers and long tusks
8. uses snout to feel along seabed to find clams to eat

Fact File About the Walrus

What is it?

What does it look like?

Where does it live?

What does it eat?

B Write a report about the walrus by yourself. Don't forget a title and subheadings, and write five sentences.

C Look over your report. Did you remember everything?

Strand: Writing Elements: Communicating LO 1; Understanding LO 5; Exploring and Using LO 6, 7

On the Ning Nang Nong

Phonics Game | ture | /ur/ sound family – er, ir, ur

A Before you begin the game, tick (✓) the sounds that you are able to read. 🖊

er		ture		wr		ear		ow		ir		sion	
nk		igh		ur		ture		ey		ph		er	

B Roll and read.

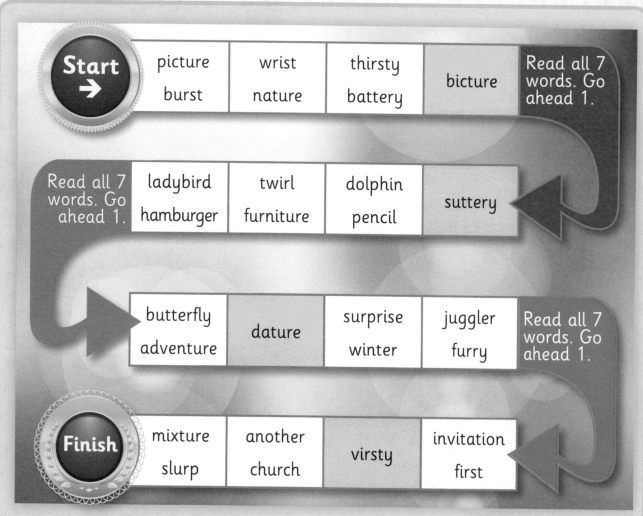

| Start → | picture / burst | wrist / nature | thirsty / battery | bicture | Read all 7 words. Go ahead 1. |

| Read all 7 words. Go ahead 1. | ladybird / hamburger | twirl / furniture | dolphin / pencil | suttery |

| butterfly / adventure | dature | surprise / winter | juggler / furry | Read all 7 words. Go ahead 1. |

| Finish | mixture / slurp | another / church | virsty | invitation / first |

Try playing this at home again. All you need is a die and a set of counters.

Poetry

On the Ning Nang Nong

On the Ning Nang Nong

Where the cows go Bong!

And the monkeys all say Boo!

There's a Nong Nang Ning

Where the trees go Ping!

And the teapots Jibber Jabber Joo.

On the Nong Ning Nang

All the mice go Clang!

And you just can't catch 'em when they do!

So it's Ning Nang Nong!

Cows go Bong!

Nong Nang Ning!

Trees go Ping!

Nong Ning Nang!

The mice go Clang!

What a noisy place to belong,

Is the Ning Nang Ning Nang Nong!!

By Spike Milligan

Strand: Reading Elements: Communicating LO 1; Understanding LO 4, 5

A In your copy, go investigate.

1. What do the monkeys say?
2. What noise do the teapots make?
3. What noise do the trees make?
4. Can you catch the mice?
5. Can you pick out four words in the poem that rhyme?

B In your copy, give your opinion.

1. If the Ning Nang Nong was a place, where do you think it might be?
2. If you lived on the Ning Nang Nong, how might you get some sleep?
3. Why do you think the trees go ping?
4. Does this poem make sense? Why do you think the poet wrote it?
5. Do you like this poem? Why?/Why not?

C Vocabulary: Ring the two words that rhyme in each set.

1. cow	noise	how	silly
2. mice	nice	hike	clock
3. goat	rich	itch	mouse
4. meet	nail	soap	rope

D Oral language: In pairs or groups, prepare a poetry performance for your class.

- Experiment with different voices, sounds and actions.
- Sounds can be made with your voice, instruments or classroom items.
- Actions can include standing, kneeling, sitting or jumping.

Strand: Reading Elements: Understanding LO 6; Exploring and Using LO 7, 8, 9
Strand: Oral Language Element: Exploring and Using LO 12

63

Phonics ture /ur/ sound family – er, ir, ur

A Read each sentence and cross out the incorrect word.

1. Mum's jeep beep got a puncture.

2. A blackbird picture chirps in a tree in our garden.

3. Robert drew a picture crayon of a monster.

4. Dad put bike all of the old garden furniture in the shed.

5. My sister got a circle new jumper and skirt.

6. We take turns when we play dice the game, Snakes and Ladders.

7. I had some toast with butter hamburger for a snack.

B Follow the instructions.

1. Cross out the last green turtle.	
2. Draw whiskers on the cat.	 
3. Draw five spots on the ladybird.	
4. Underline the picture of summer.	
5. Put a dot on the vulture.	
6. Draw a spider on the tiger's back.	  

Grammar – Capital Letters 3

A Rewrite each sentence. Add two capital letters and a full stop.

1. my brother and i like to go surfing

_____

2. today is monday and yesterday was Sunday

_____

3. tom and Emily went to spain on holidays

_____

4. i cannot wait for my summer holidays in June and july

_____

B Unscramble each sentence and rewrite it correctly.

1. go i to on wednesday football

_____

2. sister's my big name is jade

_____

3. birthday my may is in

_____

4. friend my in lives cork

_____

5. dad's day favourite the week of is friday

_____

C Dictation: Listen to your teacher and write the sentences.

1. _____

2. _____

How did you do? 🙂⚪ 😐⚪ ☹️⚪

Writing Genre – Nonsense Poem

A **Write a nonsense poem.** ✏️

Decide if your nonsense poem will be about a crazy zoo or farm. Make a list of real and nonsense words that rhyme with 'ning', 'nang' and 'nong'.

Ning		Nang		Nong	
Real Words	Nonsense Words	Real Words	Nonsense Words	Real Words	Nonsense Words

B **Plan your poem.** ✏️

Make a list of the animals and trees you will find there. What sounds will they make?

Animals and Trees	Sounds They Will Make
Animal 1:	
Animal 2:	
Animal 3:	
Trees:	

C **Think of a title.** 💭❓

Look at section A. Choose three words that rhyme.

My poem will be called:

On the _____ _____ _____

D **Write your poem and then read it to your partner and the class.** ✏️

Strand: Writing Elements: Communicating LO 1, 2; Exploring and Using LO 6, 7

Making Pancakes

12

Phonics Game | Silent **k** | Silent **h**

A Before you begin the game, tick (✓) the sounds that you are able to read. ✏️

kn		ture		ir		wr		ur		air		ph	
au		kn		eigh		ey		le		ight		are	

B A spin and a roll

We all say nonsense words!

•	••	•••	••••	•••••	••••••
knuck	bicture	knee	knofe	furniture	jarley
picture	knit	ghost	wrup	wrong	thimney
knob	knom	snugger	school	fundle	knight
kneem	exhaust	wrunkle	nature	knock	wreelt
knot	chird	thirsty	wruppy	wuggle	knuppy
third	hour	wrist	kneel	phup	spaghetti
midney	honest	knate	vature	knife	shepherd
wrost	knud	glight	wrap	field	knuption

Try playing this with two players at home. Simply rub out the words you have ringed in class. This time, Player One can underline words and Player Two can ring them. Whoever fills a column first wins!

Comprehension

In pairs, look up the **bold** words below in a dictionary.

Look out for words with a silent **k** or a silent **h** in the procedure below.

How to Make Pancakes

What you will need:			
▪ 1 cup flour ▪ 1 egg	▪ 1 cup of milk ▪ a **knob** of butter	▪ 1 banana ▪ a **handful** of strawberries	▪ honey

Steps:

1. First, put the flour, the egg and the milk into a big mixing bowl.

2. Then, **whisk** them together until you get a smooth **batter**. Make sure there are no lumps.

3. Leave the batter **to one side** for an hour.

4. Add a knob of butter to a hot frying pan and allow it to melt.

5. Next, pour a little batter onto the pan. Then, flip the pancake to cook the other side.

6. Use a knife to **slice** a banana and some strawberries. Place these on the cooked pancake.

7. Serve straight away with a **drizzle** of honey.

Strand: Reading Elements: Communicating LO 1; Understanding LO 4, 5, 6

A In your copy, go investigate.

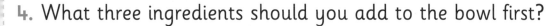

1. What do you need to make pancakes?

2. How many cups of milk do you need?

3. How much honey do you need?

4. What three ingredients should you add to the bowl first?

5. For how long should you leave the batter to one side?

6. How should the batter look after you have whisked it?

B In your copy, give your opinion.

1. Why does the butter melt in the pan?

2. Why must you flip the pancake?

3. Do you think you would need an adult to help you? Why?

4. Why do you think you should serve the pancakes straight away?

5. What else could you serve with pancakes to make them a healthy choice?

C Oral language: Find the hidden object game

The first pupil should wait outside the classroom door while the rest of the class choose a hiding place for an object. When the first pupil returns to the classroom, a second pupil must give instructions using 'bossy' verbs to help him or her find the hidden object.

Next, the second pupil should give two instructions using time words, for example: "First, walk to the whiteboard. Then, turn left."

walk   turn
find   go   sit
crawl under
jump over
pass the

Strand: Reading Elements: Understanding LO 6; Exploring and Using LO 8, 9
Strand: Oral Language Elements: Communicating LO 1; Understanding LO 4, 7

69

Phonics Silent k | Silent h

Silent k Read these words aloud. Do you hear the / k / sound?	Silent h Read these words aloud. Do you hear the / h / sound?

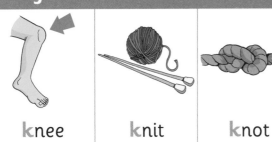

knee	knit	knot

school	ghost	gherkin

A Read each word. If the 'k' or the 'h' is silent, colour over the word. ✏️

Silent k?		Silent h?	
knit	koala	horrible	downhill
kennel	kitchen	ghost	honest
kitten	knocker	holiday	playhouse
knot	knickers	school	dinghy
kneel	knives	beehive	rhyme
knob	know	exhausted	hour

B Read each sentence and cross out the incorrect word. ✏️

1. I knelt down and bleed hurt my knee.

2. Last Hallowe'en, I dressed up as a ghost and my brother dressed up as a sheet knight.

3. I cut up the spoon spaghetti with a knife for my little sister.

4. Kevin fell and grazed his new knuckles and his knee.

5. I did not know that the show shop would be only an hour long.

6. I will knocked knock on the door of the office in school.

7. I know I will be exhausted after our hike swim up the mountain.

8. I saw a rhinoceros, a tiger and an elephant on our bus school trip to the zoo.

Strand: Reading Element: Understanding LO 4, 5, 6

Grammar – 'Bossy' (Command) Verbs

Earlier in this unit, we read a procedure telling us how to make pancakes. The procedure used lots of verbs. Some verbs give orders, such as 'stop', 'look', 'write' or 'jump'. These are **'bossy' verbs**.

A Ring only the 'bossy' verbs in the grid below.

(clean)	cleaning	hop	hopping	walked	walk
paints	paint	wash	washed	send	sending
run	ran	read	reading	rang	ring

B Choose a 'bossy' verb from the word box to complete each instruction.

dry	throw	cut	turn	put	wash	peel	paint

1. First, take turns to   the dice.

2. Then, using a paintbrush,   the piece of card red.

3. Next,   the milk and the ice-cream into a blender.

4. First, walk down the corridor and   left.

5. After that,   the banana and   it into slices.

6. Finally,   your hands and   them.

C Think of a 'bossy' verb to complete each instruction.

1. Then, add water to the sugar and   it with a spoon.

2. First, draw a circle and   it out using scissors.

3. Next, run on the spot and   the ball to your partner.

D Dictation: Listen to your teacher and write the sentences.

1. _____

2. _____

How did you do? 🙂 ⚪ 😐 ⚪ 🙁 ⚪

Writing Genre – Parts of a Procedure

A Highlight the parts of a procedure. 🔍

Turn back to the procedure, 'How to Make Pancakes' on page 68. Use yellow stickies or a highlighter pen to highlight the different parts of the procedure.

B Which of the following procedures is best, (a) or (b)?
Tick (✓) what each one does well. ✏️

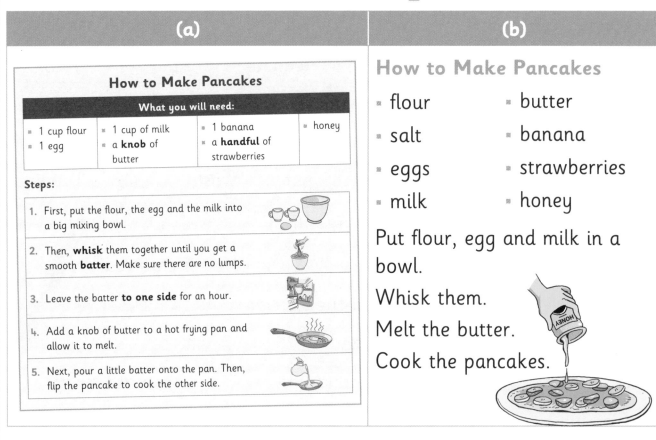

(a)

How to Make Pancakes

What you will need:

▪ 1 cup flour ▪ 1 egg	▪ 1 cup of milk ▪ a **knob** of butter	▪ 1 banana ▪ a **handful** of strawberries	▪ honey

Steps:

1. First, put the flour, the egg and the milk into a big mixing bowl.
2. Then, **whisk** them together until you get a smooth **batter**. Make sure there are no lumps.
3. Leave the batter **to one side** for an hour.
4. Add a knob of butter to a hot frying pan and allow it to melt.
5. Next, pour a little batter onto the pan. Then, flip the pancake to cook the other side.

(b)

How to Make Pancakes

- flour
- salt
- eggs
- milk
- butter
- banana
- strawberries
- honey

Put flour, egg and milk in a bowl.
Whisk them.
Melt the butter.
Cook the pancakes.

	(a)		(b)	
1. Does it have a title?	Yes	No	Yes	No
2. Does it list what you will need?	Yes	No	Yes	No
3. Does it tell you how much you need?	Yes	No	Yes	No
4. Does it number the steps?	Yes	No	Yes	No
5. Does it use time words?	Yes	No	Yes	No
6. Does it use 'bossy' verbs?	Yes	No	Yes	No

Strand: Writing **Elements:** Communicating LO 1; Exploring and Using LO 6, 8

Making a Bubble Bomb 13

Phonics Game | Silent **b** | Silent **c**

A Before you begin the game, tick (✓) the sounds that you are able to read. ✏️

kn		sion		ph		wr		ur		au		igh	
tion		le		ear		eigh		ay		ei		aw	

B Four in a row

1	2	3	4	5	6
bomb	**scent**	cromb	science	glumber	**doubt**
1	2	3	4	5	6
lamb	lomb	**climb**	**numb**	scientist	vumb
1	2	3	4	5	6
jumb	**dumb**	scont	**plumber**	pimb	**thumbnail**
1	2	3	4	5	6
scissors	**thumb**	**crumb**	scassers	**school**	**scene**
1	2	3	4	5	6
know	**hour**	scussors	**wrist**	**knob**	dramb
1	2	3	4	5	6
muscle	scint	**knob**	shumb	**wrong**	**fascinate**

Try playing this at home again. All you need is a die and a set of counters.

Comprehension

In pairs, look up the **bold** words below in a dictionary.

Look out for words with a silent **b** in the procedure below.

How to Make a Bubble Bomb

What you will need:	
• a sheet of kitchen paper	• a measuring cup
• 1 tablespoon of baking soda	• ¼ cup of warm water
• a **ziplock** plastic sandwich bag	• ½ cup of vinegar

Steps:

1. First, go outside to do this **experiment**, as it makes an awful mess.

2. Then, place the baking soda in the centre of the sheet of kitchen paper. **Wrap** the kitchen paper around the baking soda and squeeze it into a ball.

3. Next, open the ziplock bag and carefully pour in the vinegar and the warm water.

4. After that, zip the bag halfway and quickly drop the ball of kitchen paper inside it. Then, zip the bag **completely.**

5. Finally, shake the bag a little, toss it on the ground and stand back. A **reaction** will happen; the bag will puff up and **explode** with a bang, making a bubble bomb!

Strand: Reading **Elements:** Communicating LO 1; Understanding LO 4, 5, 6

A In your copy, go investigate. 🔍

1. What do you need to make a bubble bomb?

2. Where is the best place to do this experiment?

3. How much baking soda do you need?

4. How much kitchen paper do you need?

5. What two things must you place together in the ziplock bag?

6. Why must you stand back after you toss the bag on the ground?

B In your copy, give your opinion. 💭

1. Why do you think you must shake the bag?

2. Why do you think you should zip the bag halfway before dropping the kitchen paper inside?

3. How do you think you might warm the water?

4. If it was raining, where might you do this experiment instead?

5. Why do you think it is called a 'bubble bomb'?

6. Can you think of another name for this experiment?

C Vocabulary: Write the correct word. ✏️

 I thought there were three left. **were**	 **where**	**wear**

1. You must _____ a raincoat, as it is raining.

2. All of the boys _____ playing outside.

3. _____ are you going on holidays?

4. Do you know _____ Ella lives?

5. I don't know _____ I put my school bag.

6. Dad _____ a suit to work every day.

7. We _____ in First Class last year.

8. What will you _____ to the concert?

Phonics | Silent b | Silent c

Silent b
Read these words aloud. Do you hear the / b / sound?

 lamb

 crumb

 thumb

Silent c
Read these words aloud. Do you hear the / c / sound?

 scissors

 science

 muscles

A Read each word. If the 'b' or the 'c' is silent, colour over the word. ✏️

Silent b?		Silent c?	
ribbon	doubt	scent	sandcastle
climb	numb	pancake	scene
lamb	crumb	helicopter	scissors
alphabet	umbrella	science	muscle
hamburger	plumber	doctor	fascinate

B Read each sentence and cross out the incorrect word.

1. I love the scent of Mum's perfume sweet.

2. There was a most big explosion when a bomb went off.

3. Yesterday, I cut my knife thumb badly with a pair of scissors.

4. A plumber put in a new bathroom at my grandad's school house.

5. My birthday cake was so mixture delicious, there wasn't a crumb left!

6. When I grow up, I want to be a fascinate scientist.

7. I seriously doubt that we will get no homework school tonight.

8. On our school trip, we climbed up a hill and saw lots of lobster lambs in the fields below.

Grammar – Plural –'es'

If a word ends in **s**, **x**, **sh** or **ch**, we add **es** to make more than one.

Examples:

dress	fox 	bush	bench
dresses	foxes 	bushes	benches

Ⓐ Ring the correct plural for each word.

1. banana → bananas bananaes
2. sandwich → sandwichs sandwiches
3. lunchbox → lunchboxs lunchboxes
4. glass → glasses glasss
5. peach → peachs peaches
6. dish → dishs dishes

Ⓑ Write the correct word.

1. Bob left _____ on the table. **crumbs / crumbes**

2. I saw two _____ running across the road. **foxs / foxes**

3. I fell and hurt both of my _____. **knees / kneees**

4. That boy _____ me all of the time. **pushs / pushes**

5. My cat stretches and _____ its back. **archs / arches**

6. My baby sister gives sloppy _____. **kisss / kisses**

Ⓒ Dictation: Listen to your teacher and write the sentences.

1. _____

2. _____

How did you do? ☺ ◯ ☹ ◯ ☹ ◯ ◯

Writing Genre – Modelled and Shared Writing

A Plan how to make apple pop snacks.

With your class, brainstorm the time words and verbs that you will need to fill in the plan.

B In pairs, fill in the plan.

Title:

What you will need:

Ingredients	Equipment

Steps: (Tip: Don't forget to use both time words and 'bossy' verbs!)

1.

2.

3.

4.

5.

C With your class, write the procedure, 'How to Make Apple Pop Snacks'.

Cowboys and Robbers 14

Phonics Game | /oi/ sound family – oi, oy | Soft g

A Before you begin the game, tick (✓) the sounds that you are able to read. ✏️

oy		ur		wr		oi		ey		oy		ear	
er		kn		ee		ear		ey		ture		sion	

B Snakes and Ladders

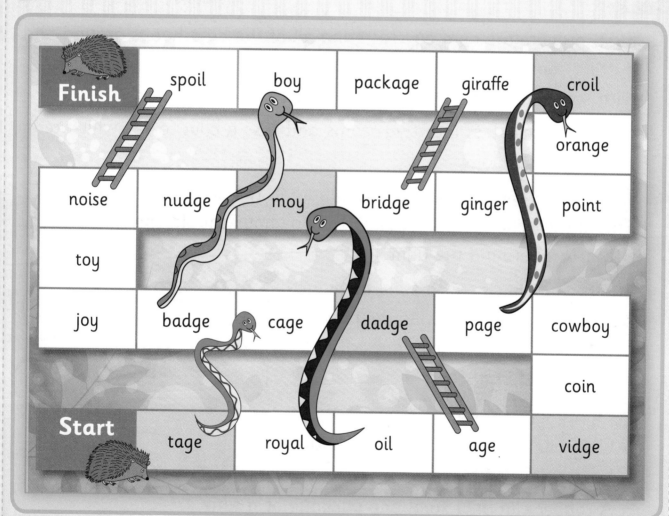

Finish	spoil	boy	package	giraffe	croil
					orange
noise	nudge	moy	bridge	ginger	point
toy					
joy	badge	cage	dadge	page	cowboy
					coin
Start	tage	royal	oil	age	vidge

> Try playing this at home again. All you need is a die and a set of counters.

Comprehension

In pairs, look up the **bold** words below in a dictionary.

Look out for words with **oi**, **oy** or soft **g** in the procedure below.

STOP

Game: Cowboys and Robbers

What you will need:		
▪ 8 hula hoops	▪ 8 cones	▪ a bucket of beanbags

Steps:

1. First, prepare the gym by scattering all of the hula hoops around and putting some beanbags inside each hula hoop. Then, make a square with some cones in the **centre** of the gym.

2. Next, split the class into two teams and toss a coin to see which team will be the cowboys.

3. The robbers should stand in the square in the centre of the gym. This is their cage or **safe zone**. The cowboys should spread out in all **directions** around the gym.

4. The robbers must try to steal as many beanbags or **packages** as they can and bring them back to their cage without being tagged by a cowboy.

5. Here are a few rules:

   ▪ Only one robber can be inside a hula hoop at a time.

   ▪ A robber can only steal one package at a time.

   ▪ A robber who is tagged by a cowboy must sit down wherever they are tagged and not **budge**. They can **re-join** the game when they are freed by another robber.

   ▪ The robbers win if they steal all of the packages.

Strand: Reading Elements: Communicating LO 1; Understanding LO 4, 5, 6

A In your copy, go investigate. 🔍

1. What do you need to play this game?

2. Where can you play this game?

3. How many hula hoops do you need?

4. How should you decide which team are cowboys and which are robbers?

5. What must the robbers do to win the game?

6. In the game, what do you pretend the beanbags are?

B In your copy, give your opinion. 💭?

1. Could you play this game somewhere else?

2. Is this game like any playground game that you have played?

3. Would you prefer to be a cowboy or a robber? Why?

4. Why do you think children would enjoy this game?

C Vocabulary: Write the correct word. ✏️

meet	**meat**	**hear**	**here**

1. Did you _____ all the noise last night?

2. I can _____ the baby crying.

3. Put your bag and coat over _____.

4. I went to the butcher to buy some _____.

5. Will I _____ you at five o'clock tomorrow?

6. The dog ran past me and hid over _____.

7. We _____ so thirsty after the race. **where / were**

8. Emily will _____ a dress to the party. **wear / where**

9. We are going on a trip _____ a farm. **to / two / too**

10. Did you get a new toy _____? **to / two / too**

Phonics | /oi/ sound family – oi, oy | Soft g

Do you remember the ways to spell the /oi/ sound?		The letter g changes to a /j/ sound (soft g) when it meets e, i or y.			
 soil	 voyage	**Hard g**		**Soft g**	
		gate	 glass	 cage	 giraffe

A Look at each picture. Tick (✓) the correct spelling.

	boil		boi		toilet
	boyl		boy		toylet
	toi		noise		joy
	toy		noyse		joi
	poison		roial		tortoyse
	poyson		royal		tortoise

B Tick (✓) the real words and ✗ the silly words.

1. germ
2. hidge
3. flidge
4. cage
5. giraffe
6. gerb
7. fage
8. mudge
9. fridge

C Fill in the correct word from the word box.

orange	gel	package	giraffe

1. On Friday, I had an apple and an _____ for lunch.

2. I meant to post a _____ to my cousin for her birthday.

3. Cian puts _____ in his hair every morning.

4. We saw an elephant and a _____ at the zoo.

Strand: Reading Element: Understanding LO 4, 5, 6

Grammar – Plural – 'ies'

What to do with words ending in 'y':

Consonant and 'y': + 's'	Consonant and 'y':
key → keys	baby → babies 
toy → toys	puppy → puppies 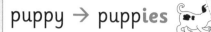

A Ring the correct plural for each word.

1.	jelly:	jellys	jellies
2.	blackberry:	blackberrys	blackberries
3.	curry:	currys	curries
4.	turkey:	turkeys	turkies
5.	cherry:	cherrys	cherries
6.	lolly:	lollys	lollies
7.	chutney:	chutneys	chutnies

B Write the correct word.

1. We saw two _____ at the zoo. **monkeys / monkies**
2. We had _____ at the cinema. **jellys / jellies**
3. I gave out the _____ in school. **copys / copies**
4. There were three _____ in the field. **donkeys / donkies**
5. My sister got new _____ for her birthday. **toys / toies**
6. We need two _____ for our shopping. **trolleys / trollies**

C Dictation: Listen to your teacher and write the sentences.

1. _____

2. _____

How did you do? ☺ ○ 😐 ○ ☹ ○

...how to make a banana blast smoothie.

...your class, brainstorm the time words and verbs that you will need to fill in the plan.

B In pairs, fill in the plan.

Title:

What you will need:

Ingredients	Equipment

Steps: (Tip: Don't forget to use both time words and 'bossy' verbs!)

1.		
2.		
3.		
4.		

C Write the procedure, 'How to Make a Banana Blast Smoothie' by yourself.

D Look over your procedure again. Did you remember everything?

Strand: Writing Elements: Communicating LO 1, 2; Exploring and Using LO 6, 7

The Gingerbread Man 15

Phonics Game /e/ sound family – ea

A Before you begin the game, tick (✓) the sounds that you are able to read. ✏️

ea		sion		ph		ew		le		al		wr	
ew		oi		kn		ie		ou		tion		le	

B Roll and read.

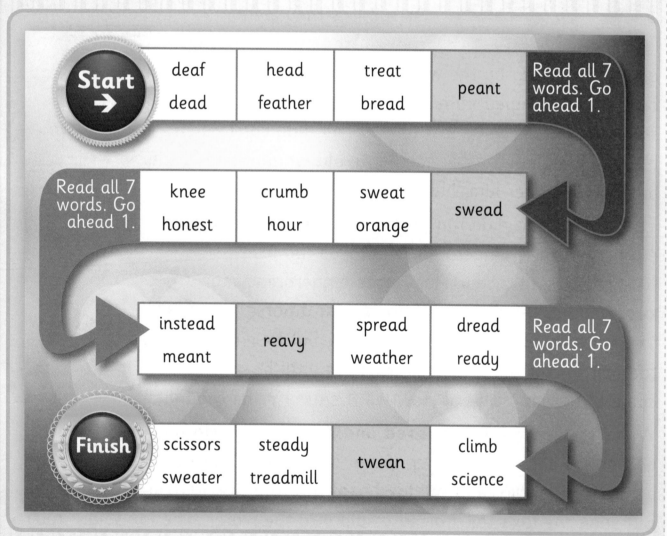

| Start → | deaf / dead | head / feather | treat / bread | peant | Read all 7 words. Go ahead 1. |

| Read all 7 words. Go ahead 1. | knee / honest | crumb / hour | sweat / orange | swead |

| instead / meant | reavy | spread / weather | dread / ready | Read all 7 words. Go ahead 1. |

| Finish | scissors / sweater | steady / treadmill | twean | climb / science |

Try playing this at home again. All you need is a die and a set of counters.

Strand: Reading Element: Understanding LO 4, 5

Comprehension

In pairs, look up the **bold** words below in a dictionary.

Sometimes the letters **ea** make the /e/ sound. Look out for words with **ea** in the story below.

The Gingerbread Man

Once upon a time, a little old woman and man lived in a cottage. One day, the little old woman made some gingerbread men.

As soon as they were cooked, she put the tray of gingerbread men by the window to cool. Suddenly, one of them jumped up and ran off down the road, shouting, "Run, run as fast as you can, you can't catch me, I'm the gingerbread man." The old woman and man chased after him, but they couldn't catch him.

The gingerbread man ran past a pig. The pig wanted to eat him, but the gingerbread man was too fast. Next, he passed a cow. Again, the gingerbread man kept running. After that, he **sped** past a horse. They all chased the gingerbread man, but he was too fast for them. He kept on running until he came to a river. "Oh no! How will I cross it?" he thought.

With that, a **sly** fox **appeared** and said, "I can help you. Sure, you are as light as a feather. Jump onto my **bushy** tail and I will swim across." So he did, and the fox **leapt** into the river and started to swim. But soon the fox's tail started to dip into the water. The fox said, "You're too heavy for my tail. Hop onto my back." Then he said, "Why, you are still too heavy. Jump onto my nose." No sooner had they reached the other side than the fox **tossed** the gingerbread man up into the air. Snap! "What a **delicious** breakfast!" he thought.

Strand: Reading Elements: Communicating LO 1; Understanding LO 4, 5, 6

A In your copy, go investigate. 🔍

1. Who lived in the cottage?

2. What did the old woman do one day?

3. What happened when the old woman put the tray by the window?

4. Who did the gingerbread man pass first?

5. Who played a trick on the gingerbread man?

6. How would you describe the fox?

B In your copy, give your opinion. 💭❓

1. Do you think the fox planned to eat the gingerbread man? Why?

2. Why did the gingerbread man decide to trust the fox?

3. If you were the gingerbread man, what would you have done?

4. What do you think would have happened if the old woman had not left the window open?

5. What do you think would have happened if the gingerbread man had tried to swim across the river by himself?

C Vocabulary: Write the correct word. ✏️

 **been** **bean** **knew**  **new**

1. Have you _____ to the zoo yet?

2. I like to eat _____s on toast for my tea.

3. I want a _____ football for my birthday.

4. I _____ all of the answers in the test.

5. Has the postman _____ here yet?

6. Handa loves her _____ red jeep.

D Oral language: Interview 💬

One pupil must pretend to be the fox from the story. The rest of the class should interview the fox and ask him lots of questions.

Strand: Reading Elements: Understanding LO 6; Exploring and Using LO 8, 9
Strand: Oral Language Elements: Communicating LO 1, 2; Exploring and Using LO 9, 11, 14

87

Phonics /e/ sound family – ea

You can spell the /e/ sound using the following letters:

 Fred

 thread

A Look at each picture. Tick (✓) the correct word.

	health head headband		bread breakfast bear		fraction furniture feather
	scissors sweater sweat		dead dread dare		head heavy hare

B Tick (✓) the real words and ✗ the nonsense words.

1. dead   ✓   2. beather   ✗   3. feather   4. spread

5. bleant   6. bread   7. breath   8. vealthy

9. head   10. inblead   11. instead   12. zeant

C Fill in the correct word from the word box.

breath	steady	meant	dread	healthy	breakfast

1. At the start of the race, Amir shouted, "Ready, _____ , go!"

2. Yesterday, I had a slice of bread for my _____ .

3. I have to bring home all of my books and I _____ lifting my heavy bag.

4. My grandad says porridge is a very _____ breakfast.

5. I forgot to wash my sweater. I _____ to do it last night.

6. It was so cold this morning that I could see my _____ as I walked to school.

Grammar – Connecting Words

Connecting words allow us to connect sentences.
Examples: and   but   because   so
Connecting words help us to improve our writing. Look at the pair of sentences below. Which one reads best?

1. It was raining all day. We couldn't go out to play.   ✗
2. It was raining all day, so we couldn't go out to play.   ✓

A Write the best connecting word to complete each sentence. ✏️

1. The bus stopped _____ I jumped off at my stop. **and / but**

2. I ran after my friend, _____ I could not catch her. **so / but**

3. It started to snow, _____ we put on our coats. **so / because**

4. I couldn't visit my gran, _____ she is sick. **so / because**

5. We got home late _____ went straight to bed. **and / but**

6. Our car broke down, _____ we were late home. **so / but**

7. I was sick yesterday, _____ I didn't go to school. **but / so**

8. Sam was supposed to come and play, _____ he was sick. **and / but**

9. Last week was the best week ever, _____ we had no school. **because / to**

10. We could not go on our trip today, _____ we will go tomorrow. **but / and**

11. The wizard cast a spell on the boy _____ turned him into a frog. **so / and**

B Dictation: Listen to your teacher and write the sentences. 👂

1. _____

2. _____

How did you do? ☺ ◯ ☺ ◯ ☹ ◯

Writing Genre – Parts of a Narrative

A **Fix the narrative.**

Read the parts of the story and number them in the correct order. (You could also photocopy this page, cut it up and put it in order with a partner.)

He ran and ran until he came to a river. "Oh no! What will I do?" he thought.	
Once upon a time, a little old woman and man lived in a cottage. The little old woman loved to bake nice things to eat, especially gingerbread men.	
Then, he met a fox. The fox offered to help him swim across, but he was a sly old fox. He tricked him into hopping onto his nose and then he tossed him up into the air and gobbled him up.	
1 **The Gingerbread Man**	
One day, the old woman left the gingerbread man to cool by the window, but the gingerbread man jumped up and ran off down the road. Soon he was chased by the old woman, the old man, a pig, a cow and a horse.	

B **Use this colour key to colour the parts of the narrative above.**

Yellow	Purple	Green	Red	Blue
Title	When Where Who	First event	Problem	Resolution

Strand: Writing Elements: Communicating LO 1; Exploring and Using LO 6, 8

Horrid Henry's Holiday 16

Phonics Game	/or/ sound family – or, ore	/air/ sound family – air

A Tick (✓) the sounds that you are able to read.

or		ea		oy		le		ew		ore		tion	
ch		kn		wr		ey		air		sion		ear	

B A spin and a roll

We all say nonsense words!

forgive	anchor	wrost	naggle	noportint	injection
blormy	glore	more	inwention	chemical	store
stormy	important	twore	wrinkle	pemtion	forhome
school	vear	bear	chemist	dictionary	snore
loch	smore	chemist	chamical	character	nonchor
boch	deavy	pleasant	clord	ache	girunt
giraffe	seahorse	score	yich	gelm	churacter
heavy	mechanic	wrist	wrinkle	wralt	knult

Try playing this with two players at home. Simply rub out the words you have circled in class. This time, Player One can underline words and Player Two can ring them. Whoever fills a column first wins!

Strand: Reading Element: Understanding LO 4, 5

Comprehension

In pairs, look up the **bold** words below in a dictionary.

Look out for words with **or** or **ore** in the story below.

Horrid Henry's Holiday

Around four o'clock on Day Five, the family **huddled** inside the cold, **damp**, smelly tent listening to the howling wind and the pouring rain.

"Time for a walk!" said Dad.

"Great idea!" said Mum, sneezing. "I'll get the boots."

"Great idea!" said Peter, sneezing. "I'll get the **macs**."

"But it's pouring outside," said Henry.

"So?" said Dad. "What better time to go for a walk?"

"I'm not coming," said Horrid Henry.

"I am," said Perfect Peter. "I don't mind the rain."

Dad **poked** his head outside the tent. "The rain has stopped," he said. "I'll **remake** the fire."

"I'm not coming," said Henry.

"We need more **firewood**," said Dad. "Henry can stay here and collect some. And make sure it's dry."

Henry poked his head outside the tent. The rain had stopped, but the sky was still cloudy. The fire spat. *I won't go*, thought Henry. *The forest will be all muddy and wet.* He looked round to see if there was any wood closer to home. That was when he saw the thick, dry wooden pegs holding up all the tents. Henry looked to the left. Henry looked to the right. No one was around. *If I just take a few pegs from each tent*, he thought, *they'll never be missed.* When Mum and Dad came back they were delighted.

"What a lovely roaring fire," said Mum.

"Clever you to find some dry wood," said Dad.

The wind blew. Henry dreamed he was floating in a cold river, floating, floating, floating. He woke up. He shook his head. He *was* floating. The tent was filled with cold muddy water. Then the tent **collapsed** on top of them.

(From 'Horrid Henry's Holiday' by Francesca Simon)

A In your copy, go investigate. 🔍

1. Where did Horrid Henry and his family go on holidays?

2. What did Mum, Dad and Perfect Peter want to do?

3. Why did Henry not want to collect firewood in the forest?

4. What did Henry use instead of firewood?

5. How did Mum and Dad feel when they came back to find the fire lighting?

6. What happened to the tent when a big gust of wind came along?

B In your copy, give your opinion. 💭?

1. Would Henry have taken the pegs if there was someone around? Why?

2. Would you like to go on a camping holiday? Why/Why not?

3. How do you think the other campers felt when their tents collapsed?

4. How do you think the other campers treated Henry and his family?

5. What do you think Henry and his family did next?

C Vocabulary: Write the correct word. ✏️

ate	**eight**	**our**	**hour**

1. My cat had _____ kittens last night.

2. I will be _____ years old next week.

3. On Monday, I _____ a slice of chocolate cake.

4. That is _____ puppy. His name is Sammy.

5. Mum will be home in an _____.

6. We saw a stray cat in _____ garden.

7. Would you like a _____ car? **knew / new**

8. I have _____ very good in school. **been / bean**

Phonics /or/ sound family – or, ore | /air/ sound family – air

You can spell the /or/ sound using the following letters:	
horse	 core

You can spell the /air/ sound using the following letters:		
bear	hair	hare

A Nonsense words: Read the words. Ring the real words.

1	2	3	4	5	6
hair	pair	sairy	funfair	porse	snore
horse	chair	horget	fair	chore	fairy
nair	gairy	stormy	thorny	forture	torture
slair	hairy	blormy	gairy	morture	smore
forgot	airbort	airport	florny	anymore	wheelchair

B Tick (✓) the correct word for each sentence.

1. My little sister's favourite _____ is 'The Little Fairy'.
   short ___ story ___ sport ___

2. I must go to the _____ to get my hair cut.
   hairbrush ___ hairy ___ hairdresser ___

3. I got a new _____ of runners in town on Saturday.
   porch ___ pair ___ pork ___

4. I got into trouble when my younger brother hit me. It is so
   _____. uniform ___ upstairs ___ unfair ___

5. We picked my gran up from the _____ late last night.
   airy ___ airport ___ airline ___

6. I play football, basketball and tennis. I love playing _____.
   sports ___ story ___ shorts ___

7. When you travel abroad you need to bring a _____.
   port ___ popcorn ___ passport ___

Strand: Reading Element: Understanding LO 4, 5, 6

Grammar – Speech Marks

"Can I have that, please?"

We use speech marks when writing to show what someone has said. We put the speech marks around the exact words spoken.

Examples: "Can I have that, please?" asked Adil.
The sad girl cried, "But I don't want to go."

A Are these speech marks used correctly? Write ✓ or ✗.

1. "Stop that," said Mum.

2. "Stop it shouted Pat".

3. "What time is it?" asked Jane.

4. Ben hit me "said" Ginger.

B Put speech marks in the correct places in these sentences.

1. I don't want dinner, moaned Kate.

2. I love my puppy, squealed Emily.

3. I'll come visit tomorrow, said Joe.

4. Ben hit me, shouted Amir.

5. I hate homework, groaned Chung.

C In your copy, rewrite these sentences correctly.

Remember: Use speech marks, capital letters, a comma and a full stop.

1. we will go visit janka tomorrow said mum

2. we must be quiet whispered calum

3. i've a pain in my tummy moaned tessa

4. my little brother cheered I love going to the park

D Dictation: Listen to your teacher and write the sentences.

1. _____

2. _____

How did you do? ☺ ◯ 😐 ◯ ☹ ◯

Writing Genre – Modelled and Shared Writing

A In pairs, use the story planner to plan a story.

Story Planner

When?	One dark night	Long, long ago	Early one summer morning	Once upon a time
Where?	hidden cave	magical forest	old cottage	space rocket
Who?	mad robot	friendly witch	nasty pirate	beautiful princess
First event	cast a spell	bumped into a ...	launched a spaceship	was turned into a ...
Problem	got lost	crashed into a planet	was captured	was chased
Resolution	?	?	?	?

Title:	
When? Where? Who?	**The first event**
The problem	**The resolution**

B With your class, pick one story to write together.
  Don't forget to use connecting words and speech marks.

Strand: Writing Elements: Communicating LO 1, 2; Exploring and Using LO 6, 7

The Dinosaur's Dinner 17

Vocabulary – Revision of Homophones

A Tricky words: Match each pair of words that sound alike.

	to	their			wear	eight	
	see	wood			right	bean	
	there	bee			hear	write	
	would	two			meet	knew	
	be	witch			been	where	
	hour	sea			new	here	
	which	our			ate	meat	

B Write the correct word.

1. I cannot wait to   my aunty tomorrow. **see / sea**

2. We went on a mini-beast hunt and I saw a   . **be / bee**

3. Will you put the basket over   , please? **there / their**

4. Dad collected   for the campfire. **would / wood**

5. We went on   school trip last week. **hour / our**

6.   you be able to help me, please? **would / wood**

7. "Will you   here next week?" asked Feena. **be / bee**

8. It took an   to drive to Granny's house. **hour / our**

9.   are you going on your summer holidays? **wear / where**

10. "Go down there and turn   ," said Roman. **right / write**

11. Did you   the girl singing? **hear / here**

Comprehension

In pairs, look up the **bold** words below in a dictionary.

STOP

The Dinosaur's Dinner

Once a mighty dinosaur
Came to **dine** with me,
He gobbled up the curtains
And swallowed our **settee**.

He didn't seem to fancy
Onion soup with crusty bread,
He much preferred the **flavour**
Of our furniture instead.

He ate up all our dining chairs
And carpets from the floor
He **polished off** the table, then
He looked around for more.

The television disappeared
In one almighty gulp,
Wardrobes, beds and bathroom
He crunched into a **pulp**.

He really loved the greenhouse
He liked the garden shed,
He started on the chimney pots
But then my mother said:

Your friends are always welcome
To drop in for a bite,
But really this one seems to have
A giant **appetite**.

You'd better take him somewhere
  else,
I'm sure I don't know where,
I only know this friend of yours
Needs more than we can **spare**!

And suddenly I **realised**
I knew the very place,
And when I showed him where it
  was
You should have seen his face –

I don't think I've seen anyone
Enjoy a dinner more,
I watched him wander on his way,
A happy dinosaur!

The **council** did **rebuild** our school,
But that of course took time.
And all because a dinosaur
Came home with me to dine!

By June Crebbin

A In your copy, go investigate. 🔍

1. Who came to visit for dinner?

2. Can you list three things that the dinosaur ate inside the house?

3. What did the dinosaur eat in the garden?

4. Who said that the dinosaur had to leave?

5. Where did the boy's mother tell him to take the dinosaur?

6. Where did the boy take the dinosaur next?

7. Who had to rebuild the school?

B In your copy, give your opinion. 💭❓

1. Why do you think the boy's mother said the dinosaur had to leave?

2. Where do you think the boy found the dinosaur?

3. Why do you think the boy did not seem worried about the dinosaur eating the furniture?

4. How do you think the dinosaur felt when he saw the school?

5. How do you think the pupils felt about what happened to their school?

C Oral language 💬

Do this activity in groups of four. You must retell the story of the poem, 'The Dinosaur's Dinner', in your own words.

- First, take a sheet of paper. The first pupil should write the first sentence on the top line. Remember to set the scene and introduce the characters. Then, pass it on to the next pupil to write the next line.

- When you have finished, read your story to your group and the class.

Strand: Reading Element: Exploring and Using LO 8, 9
Strand: Oral Language Elements: Communicating LO 1; Understanding LO 4, 5, 7; Exploring and Using LO 11

99

Phonics /k/ sound family – ch

You can spell the /k/ sound using the following letters:

car	kite	black	school

A Match each word to its meaning.

school	someone who repairs (fixes) cars
anchor	someone who draws the plans for building houses
mechanic	a shop where medicine can be bought
architect	a place where children go to learn
chemist	a metal object that stops a boat from floating away

B Fill in the correct word/s from the word box.

toothache	character	chemicals	school
orchestra	mechanic	chemist	playschool

1. Dad had to bring the jeep to the garage for the _____ to fix it.

2. An _____ played at our school last week.

3. My little sister goes to _____ every morning.

4. Dad keeps a container of weed-killer in the shed along with the other _____ .

5. Friday is my favourite day in _____ , because we get no homework.

6. I loved the _____ , Mrs Trunchball, in the book, 'Matilda'.

7. When I had a _____ , Dad went to the _____ to get something to ease the pain.

Strand: Reading Element: Understanding LO 4, 5, 6

Make your stories more interesting by using different words for 'said'.

Grammar – Tired Words – 'said'

A Fill in the best word from the word box.

cackled	whispered	cheered	sobbed
boasted	giggled	asked	roared

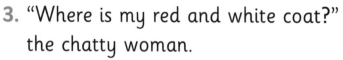
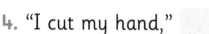

1. "Fee, fi, fo, fum!" _____ the big giant.

2. "We must be quiet," _____ the little girl.

3. "Where is my red and white coat?" _____ the chatty woman.

4. "I cut my hand," _____ the small boy.

5. "Ha, ha, ha!" _____ the wicked witch.

6. "That is the funniest joke ever," _____ the little girl.

7. "Go on, you can do it!" _____ the whole class.

8. "I have five new footballs," _____ the spoilt boy.

B The sentences above used adjectives. List some of them below.

1. _____ 2. _____ 3. _____ 4. _____

5. _____ 6. _____ 7. _____ 8. _____

C Complete these sentences in your copy. Try to use adjectives where you can. Don't forget speech marks.

1. … shouted the old man.   2. … groaned the tired little girl.

3. … cried the little mouse.   4. … whispered the friendly giant.

D Dictation: Listen to your teacher and write the sentences.

1. _____

2. _____

How did you do? 🙂 ⬤ 😐 ⬤ ☹ ⬤

Writing Genre – Independent Writing

A Plan a story. ✏️

Plan a story about an imaginary creature coming to school. Use the story planner on page 96 to help you plan a story. Fill in the plan below.

Title:

When? Where? Who? 🕐 🗺️ 🧑	The first event
The problem 👩❓❓🧑	**The resolution** 💡🧑

Ring some time words to help you.

> Once upon a time   this morning   a long, long time ago   first
> next   then   after that   soon   later on   finally   at last

Connecting words:	Other words for 'said':	Can you think of any more?
and because but so	yelled sobbed roared whispered pleaded asked shouted begged	_____ _____ _____ _____ _____ _____

B Write the story by yourself. Use the plan above to help you. ✏️   🄿

C Look over your story again. Did you remember everything? 🄿

Strand: Writing Elements: Communicating LO 1, 2; Exploring and Using LO 6, 7

Revision

Day 1

1. Correct the three mistakes in each sentence.

(a) shane and i love chocolate cake

(b) mum went on a trip to brussels

2. Is the underlined word an adjective, a noun or a verb?

(a) We had a <u>lovely</u> time at Jack's.

Adjective   Noun   Verb

(b) Do you <u>know</u> Adam and Joey?

Adjective   Noun   Verb

(c) That is a very big <u>box</u>.

Adjective   Noun   Verb

3. Write more than one.

(a) one doll   two

(b) one bench   two

(c) one fox   two

(d) one brush   two

4. Tick the real words.

package   sphere

airbag   knisp

puffature   quotty

princess   rough

Day 2

1. Correct the three mistakes in each sentence.

(a) luke and jane are coming to my house

(b) dara's birthday is in june

2. Is the underlined word an adjective, a noun or a verb?

(a) The little rabbit <u>ran</u> away.

Adjective   Noun   Verb

(b) We went swimming in the <u>pool</u>.

Adjective   Noun   Verb

(c) My bedroom is very <u>messy</u>.

Adjective   Noun   Verb

3. Write more than one.

(a) one box   two

(b) one table   two

(c) one witch   two

(d) one dish   two

4. Tick the real words.

mechanic   skone

confusion   newsletter

losture   coward

mouch   preenull

Revision: Grammar and Phonics

Day 3

1. **Is the underlined word an adjective, a noun or a verb?**

   (a) Will you open the <u>door</u>, please?

   Adjective ☐   Noun ☐   Verb ☐

   (b) That new film is very <u>funny</u>.

   Adjective ☐   Noun ☐   Verb ☐

   (c) I <u>love</u> my pet dog, Amber.

   Adjective ☐   Noun ☐   Verb ☐

2. **Write more than one.**

   (a) one wish   two _____

   (b) one cherry   two _____

   (c) one nappy   two _____

   (d) one bath   two _____

3. **Add speech marks to each sentence.**

   (a)   I will come too,   shouted Lan.

   (b)   I can help as well,   said Liam.

4. **Tick the real words.**

   knight ☐   zeant ☐

   threat ☐   scribble ☐

   fascinate ☐   exhaust ☐

   gersh ☐   cleebair ☐

Day 4

1. **Is the underlined word an adjective, a noun or a verb?**

   (a) Dad <u>stored</u> the ladder in the shed.

   Adjective ☐   Noun ☐   Verb ☐

   (b) I like going to <u>Dublin</u>.

   Adjective ☐   Noun ☐   Verb ☐

   (c) That parrot is awfully <u>noisy</u>.

   Adjective ☐   Noun ☐   Verb ☐

2. **Write more than one.**

   (a) one berry   two _____

   (b) one six   two _____

   (c) one toy   two _____

   (d) one lolly   two _____

3. **Add speech marks to each sentence.**

   (a)   I would love that, squealed Abbie.

   (b)   Let's do that now, roared Daniel.

4. **Tick the real words.**

   crowbob ☐   wheelie ☐

   briefcase ☐   joyful ☐

   ignore ☐   scarecrow ☐

   grustration ☐   permonsion ☐

Assessment: Phonics

A Read each sentence and cross out the incorrect word.

1. I loaned my red pencil to my friend in office school.

2. My little sister likes to climb into the shopping trolley cookie at the supermarket.

3. Would you like to be a mechanic hawk or an architect when you grow up?

4. "I dread running doing all of my chores this evening," moaned Ella.

5. I had a slice of toast and some crumbs orange juice for breakfast.

6. I knit a scissors scarf for my gran and wrote her a card for her birthday.

7. I do not know big that little boy over there.

8. I meant fell and grazed my head and my knee.

9. Did you see the big circus tent set up in the lawn field?

10. My little brother is learning to how to do subtraction sums in school.

11. We will visit our relations over the summer days holidays.

12. When Dad got lost in the car, we had to stop and ask for diesel directions.

13. In my house, we are always fighting headache over what to watch on the television.

14. My younger brother is always getting into punches trouble in school.

15. Mum said it is very rude to giggle gobble your food.

Assessment: Comprehension

Grandad's Mad Garden

It was Saturday morning and I was helping Grandad clear up his garden. Grandad was a bit mad. He spent hours looking at things that weren't really there, or arguing with the radio, so he didn't have much time to look after his garden. I cut back some bushes and found a headlight.

"Grandad!" I called. "I've found your car!"

"So you did, Lenny," he said, coming over. "I wondered where that got to."

We cut all the bushes away and there sat his old car, which had gone missing a few years ago.

"You need to get a gardener or something," I said.

"Yes, I do," he nodded. Then his eyes opened wide and he slapped his head.

"Holy smoke, Lenny!" he said. "My brother, Rupert, sent me a gardener from Japan! I forgot all about it."

Now, as I said, Grandad was a bit mad, but he did have a brother named Rupert and Rupert spent his time sailing all around the world. He often sent weird stuff back to Grandad, but when Grandad said he sent a gardener, I thought he was making things up again. He took me into the house and down to the cellar. The place was crammed with all sorts of stuff. Under a load of boxes, there was a package from Rupert. It had stamps all over it and a note from Great Uncle Rupert attached to it.

It said:

Hello from Japan!
Here's something
to clear up your
garden.
Don't let it have
any nuts!
Rupert.

We opened the box and there was a robot folded inside.

(From 'Grandad's Mad Garden' by Oisín McGann)

Assessment: Comprehension and Vocabulary

A In your copy, go investigate. 🔍

1. Who was Lenny helping in the garden?

2. How did Lenny describe Grandad?

3. Why did Grandad not have time to look after his garden?

4. When had Grandad's car gone missing?

5. What did Lenny suggest that Grandad should get to help him?

6. What did Rupert spend all of his time doing?

7. What kind of presents did Rupert send to Grandad?

B In your copy, give your opinion. 💭?

1. Why did Grandad slap his head when he remembered the package?

2. Had Grandad opened the package before? How do you know?

3. What type of gardener do you think Lenny meant for Grandad to get?

4. Do you think a robot gardener would be useful? Why?

5. What do you think might happen if you gave the robot nuts?

C Vocabulary: Write the correct word. ✏️

1. That _bee_ nearly stung me. **be / bee**

2. Did you _meet_ Sarka at the park? **meet / meat**

3. We have only _eight_ days left in school. **ate / eight**

4. I got a _new_ swimsuit for my holidays. **knew / new**

5. Have you _been_ to see the new film yet? **been / bean**

6. _Would_ you like some ice-cream? **would / wood**

7. Put your coats and bags over _here_. **here / hear**

8. What colour is _their_ new car? **there / their**

9. You must _wear_ sun lotion in summer. **where / wear**

10. We will go to the zoo on _our_ school trip. **our / hour**

Assessment: Grammar

A Ring the words that need a capital letter.

1. my name is charlie. i live in pine woods in dublin.
2. i have two brothers named alex and jamie.
3. we have two pet rabbits, bops and bella.
4. i play football for pine woods united and i train every wednesday and saturday.
5. my birthday is in august.

B Is the underlined word an adjective, a verb or a noun?

1. I will run in the <u>egg</u> and spoon race on sports day.	Adjective	Verb	Noun
2. Our teacher gave us a <u>tricky</u> test yesterday.	Adjective	Verb	Noun
3. Would you like some <u>fresh</u> strawberries and cream?	Adjective	Verb	Noun
4. I cannot <u>wait</u> to get my summer holidays.	Adjective	Verb	Noun

C Vocabulary: Write the correct word.

1. We had to get two _____. **buss / buses / busies**
2. My aunt minds three _____. **babys / babyes / babies**
3. I scored three _____. **goals / goales / goalies**
4. Josh put the _____ in the shed. **boxes / boxies**
5. Tom gave me some _____. **jellys / jellyes / jellies**

D Add speech marks at the correct parts of each sentence.

1. I'm just fed up of this, moaned Luke.
2. I really hate doing homework, whispered Aoife.
3. Stand over there, ordered the principal.
4. Let's have some ice-cream, Feng suggested.

How did you do? ☺ ○ ☹ ○ ☹ ○

Dictation

Red indicates phonics covered in the unit. Green indicates grammar.

Purple indicates an additional activity or a question revising grammar taught recently.

Differentiation

For weaker pupils, it is possible to shorten any of the dictation sentences to as little as three words, e.g. Gran had a cup of coffee and a muffin. ➜ Gran had a cup of coffee. ➜ Gran had a coffee. ➜ cup of coffee

Unit 1

1. Gran had a cup of coffee and a muffin.
2. Mum likes to plant trees in the garden.

Unit 2

1. Sally made a cheesecake for her granny.
2. Dave gave a scream when he had a bad dream.

Why do 'Sally' and 'Dave' get a capital letter?

Unit 3

1. I think I might have left my coat at home.
2. I can ride my yellow bike on Oak Tree Road.

How many verbs can you find in each sentence?

Can you change the verb 'ride' to another suitable verb?

Why does 'Oak Tree Road' get capital letters?

Unit 4

1. Last September, I found the clue to win a prize.
2. The clown threw a bag of flour at Sam and June.

How many verbs are there in each sentence?

Can you think of another suitable verb for 'found' / 'threw'?

Why do 'September', 'Sam' and 'June' get a capital letter?

Unit 5

1. Last night, I jumped in a puddle with my cousin.
2. Then, I got into big trouble with my aunt.

Ring the verb in sentences 1 and 2.

Can you change the verb 'jump' to another suitable verb?

Change the verb 'jumped' / 'got' to the present tense.

Are there any time words in these sentences? What are they?

Unit 6

1. Yesterday, I watched television after I finished my homework.
2. Today, Jan gave out invitations to her birthday party.

How many capital letters are there in sentence 1 / sentence 2?

What words always get a capital letter?

Unit 7

1. Last week, I saw a dolphin and an elephant at the zoo.
2. Later on, I saw eight reindeer in a big stable.

Ring two nouns in sentences 1 and 2.

Ring the verb in sentence 1. Can you think of another suitable verb?

Can you find time words in sentences 1 and 2? Can you think of other suitable time words?

Unit 9

1. <u>O</u>n <u>S</u>unday, <u>P</u>au<u>l</u> had a sm<u>all</u> sli<u>c</u>e of chocolate i<u>c</u>e-cream<u>.</u>

2. <u>I</u> s<u>aw</u> a silly clown do tricks with a b<u>ear</u> at the <u>c</u>ircus<u>.</u>

Ring the adjectives in sentences 1 and 2.

Can you change the adjective 'silly' to another suitable adjective?

Unit 10

1. <u>O</u>n <u>F</u>riday, <u>I</u> will <u>wr</u>ap the big box of yummy cook<u>ies</u>.

2. <u>L</u>ast <u>J</u>une, <u>I</u> hurt my <u>wr</u>ist playing a game of hock<u>ey</u>.

Ring the two adjectives in sentence 1.

Unit 11

1. <u>D</u>id you ev<u>er</u> get a punc<u>ture</u> on your new bike<u>?</u>

2. <u>I</u> saw a spid<u>er</u> run v<u>er</u>y fast across our na<u>ture</u> table<u>.</u>

Can you find the adjective in sentence 2?

Can you add a suitable adjective for the noun 'spider'?

Unit 12

1. <u>Wear</u> the scarf that <u>G</u>ran <u>kn</u>itted<u>.</u>

2. <u>Where</u> did you put the <u>kn</u>ife<u>?</u>

Can you find the 'bossy' verb in sentence 1? Can you think of another 'bossy' verb?

Can you explain why you used 'wear' in sentence 1 and 'where' in sentence 2?

Unit 13

1. <u>I</u> cut my thum<u>b</u> using the sharp scissors<u>.</u>

2. <u>W</u>e clim<u>b</u>ed up the hill and saw a lot of lam<u>bs.</u>

Why does the plural of 'lamb' get 's'?

Ring two verbs in sentence 2. In which tense are they?

Can you change 'climbed' / 'saw' to a 'bossy' verb?

Unit 14

1. <u>F</u>irst, b<u>oil</u> the cranberr<u>ies.</u>

2. <u>N</u>ext, cut the oran<u>ges</u> and add them to the cranberr<u>ies.</u>

Why does the plural of 'cranberry' get 'ies' and the plural of 'orange' get 's'?

Ring the two command ('bossy') verbs in sentence 2.

Unit 15

1. <u>I</u> spr<u>ea</u>d the butter on the slice of br<u>ea</u>d<u>.</u>

2. <u>T</u>he box was very h<u>ea</u>vy, because Dad had put all of his tools into it<u>.</u>

Can you find the connecting words in sentences 1 and 2?

Can you find the adjective in sentence 2?

Unit 16

1. "<u>I</u> would like some m<u>ore</u> cake<u>,</u>" <u>said</u> Alex<u>.</u>

2. "<u>I</u> hate doing my b<u>oring</u> ch<u>ores,</u>" <u>moaned</u> Alan<u>.</u>

Did you remember to use speech marks?

Ring the adjective in sentence 2. Underline all of the verbs.

Unit 17

1. <u>W</u>e all moaned, "<u>N</u>ow we have to go back to s<u>ch</u>ool<u>."</u>

2. "<u>C</u>lean your room upstairs<u>,</u>" ordered Mum<u>.</u>

What words were used instead of 'said'? Can you think of other words to use for 'said'?

Did you remember to use speech marks?